VIRTUAL CHEMLAB

PROBLEMS AND ASSIGNMENTS FOR THE VIRTUAL LABORATORY 2.5

BRIAN F. WOODFIELD | MATTHEW C. ASPLUND
Brigham Young University

STEVEN HADERLIE
Springville High School

D0709635

PETRUCCI HARWOOD HERRING MADURA

GENERAL CHEMISTRY

PRINCIPLES & MODERN APPLICATIONS

NINTH EDITION

PEARSON
Prentice Hall

Upper Saddle River, NJ 07458

Project Manager: Kristen Kaiser
Senior Editor: Kent Porter-Hamann
Editor-in-Chief, Science: Dan Kaveney
Executive Managing Editor: Kathleen Schiaparelli
Assistant Managing Editor: Karen Bosch
Production Editor: Gina M. Cheselka
Supplement Cover Manager: Paul Gourhan
Supplement Cover Designer: Christopher Kossa
Manufacturing Buyer: Ilene Kahn
Manufacturing Manager: Alexis Heydt-Long

© 2007 Pearson Education, Inc.
Pearson Prentice Hall
Pearson Education, Inc.
Upper Saddle River, NJ 07458

All rights reserved. No part of this book may be reproduced in any form or by any means, without permission in writing from the publisher.

Pearson Prentice Hall™ is a trademark of Pearson Education, Inc.

The author and publisher of this book have used their best efforts in preparing this book. These efforts include the development, research, and testing of the theories and programs to determine their effectiveness. The author and publisher make no warranty of any kind, expressed or implied, with regard to these programs or the documentation contained in this book. The author and publisher shall not be liable in any event for incidental or consequential damages in connection with, or arising out of, the furnishing, performance, or use of these programs.

This work is protected by United States copyright laws and is provided solely for teaching courses and assessing student learning. Dissemination or sale of any part of this work (including on the World Wide Web) will destroy the integrity of the work and is not permitted. The work and materials from it should never be made available except by instructors using the accompanying text in their classes. All recipients of this work are expected to abide by these restrictions and to honor the intended pedagogical purposes and the needs of other instructors who rely on these materials.

Printed in the United States of America

10 9 8 7 6 5

ISBN 0-13-221075-4

Pearson Education Ltd., *London*
Pearson Education Australia Pty. Ltd., *Sydney*
Pearson Education Singapore, Pte. Ltd.
Pearson Education North Asia Ltd., *Hong Kong*
Pearson Education Canada, Inc., *Toronto*
Pearson Educación de Mexico, S.A. de C.V.
Pearson Education—Japan, *Tokyo*
Pearson Education Malaysia, Pte. Ltd.

Table of Contents

Overview 1
Getting Started 3
System Requirements 5
Installing *Virtual ChemLab* 5
Important Usage Notes and Issues 6

VCL 1-1: Measuring Mass 7
VCL 1-2: Measuring Temperature 9
VCL 1-3: Calculating Density 11

VCL 2-1: Thomson Cathode Ray Tube Experiment 13
VCL 2-2: Millikan Oil Drop Experiment 15
VCL 2-3: Investigating the Properties of Alpha and Beta Particles 19
VCL 2-4: Rutherford's Backscattering Experiment 21
VCL 2-5: Counting Atoms 25
VCL 2-6: Counting Atoms 27
VCL 2-7: Counting Atoms 29
VCL 2-8: Counting Protons, Neutrons, and Electrons 31
VCL 2-9: Counting Protons, Neutrons, and Electrons 33

VCL 3-1: Counting Molecules 35
VCL 3-2: Counting Molecules 37
VCL 3-3: Names and Formulas of Ionic Compounds 39

VCL 5-1: Strong and Weak Electrolytes 41
VCL 5-2: Writing Balanced Precipitation Reactions 43
VCL 5-3: Precipitation Reactions 45
VCL 5-4: Concepts in Acid-Base Titrations 47
VCL 5-5: Acid-Base Titration: Practice 49
VCL 5-6: Acid-Base Titration: Unknown HCl 51

VCL 6-1: Boyle's Law: Pressure and Volume 53
VCL 6-2: Charles's Law: Temperature and Volume 55
VCL 6-3: Avogadro's Law: Moles and Volume 57
VCL 6-4: Derivation of the Ideal Gas Law 59
VCL 6-5: Dalton's Law of Partial Pressures 61
VCL 6-6: Ideal vs. Real Gases 63
VCL 6-7: The Effect of Mass on Pressure 65

VCL 7-1: Specific Heat of Pb 67
VCL 7-2: Specific Heat of Al 69

VCL 7-3: Endothermic vs. Exothermic 71
VCL 7-4: Heat of Combustion: Sugar 73
VCL 7-5: Heat of Combustion: Chicken Fat 75
VCL 7-6: Heat of Combustion: TNT 77
VCL 7-7: Heat of Reaction: NaOH(aq) + HCl(aq) 79
VCL 7-8: Heat of Reaction: MgO(s) + HCl(aq) 81
VCL 7-9: Hess's Law 83
VCL 7-10: Heat of Formation: Aspirin 87
VCL 7-11: Heat of Formation: Ethanol 89

VCL 8-1: Flame Tests for Metals 91
VCL 8-2: Atomic Emission Spectra 93
VCL 8-3: Emission Spectra for Sodium and Mercury 95
VCL 8-4: Blackbody Radiation 97
VCL 8-5: Photoelectric Effect 101
VCL 8-6: The Rydberg Equation 103
VCL 8-7: Heisenberg Uncertainty Principle 105

VCL 12-1: Heat of Vaporization of Water 109
VCL 12-2: The Boiling Point of Water at High Altitude 111
VCL 12-3: Heat of Fusion of Water 113

VCL 13-1: Creating a Solution of Known Molarity 115
VCL 13-2: Creating a Solution of Known Molality 117
VCL 13-3: Converting Concentrations to Different Units 119
VCL 13-4: Enthalpy of Solution: NH_4NO_3 121
VCL 13-5: Freezing Point Depression 123
VCL 13-6: Boiling Point Elevation 125
VCL 13-7: Molar Mass Determination by Freezing Point Depression 127
VCL 13-8: Molar Mass Determination by Boiling Point Elevation 129
VCL 13-9: Changes in the Boiling Point 131

VCL 16-1: Ionization Constants of Weak Acids 133
VCL 16-2: Acid-Base Classification of Salts 135
VCL 16-3: Ranking Salt Solutions by pH 137

VCL 17-1: Predicting the Equivalence Point 139
VCL 17-2: Predicting the Equivalence Point 141
VCL 17-3: Predicting the Equivalence Point 143
VCL 17-4: Study of Acid-Base Titrations – Monoprotic Acids 145
VCL 17-5: Weak Acid-Strong Base Titrations 147
VCL 17-6: Strong Acid-Weak Base Titrations 149
VCL 17-7: Weak Acid-Weak Base Titrations 151
VCL 17-8: Study of Acid-Base Titrations – Polyprotic Acids 153
VCL 17-9: Acid-Base Standardization 155
VCL 17-10: Analysis of Baking Soda 157

VCL 18-1: Identification of Cations in Solution – Flame Tests 159
VCL 18-2: Identification of Cations in Solution – Ag^+, Hg_2^{2+}, Pb^{2+} 161
VCL 18-3: Identification of Cations in Solution – Co^{2+}, Cr^{3+}, Cu^{2+} 163
VCL 18-4: Identification of Cations in Solution – Ba^{2+}, Sr^{2+}, Ca^{2+}, Mg^{2+} 165

VCL 18-5: Identification of Cations in Solution – Co^{2+}, Cu^{2+}, Ni^{2+} 167

VCL 19-1: The Balance Between Enthalpy and Entropy 169

VCL 20-1: Study of Oxidation-Reduction Titrations 171
VCL 20-2: Standardization of a Permanganate Solution 173
VCL 20-3: Analysis of a Ferrous Chloride Sample 175

Overview

Welcome to *Virtual ChemLab: General Chemistry Laboratories*, a set of realistic and sophisticated simulations covering the topics in general chemistry. In these laboratories, students are put into a virtual environment where they are free to make the choices and decisions that they would confront in an actual laboratory setting and, in turn, experience the resulting consequences. These laboratories include simulations of inorganic qualitative analysis, fundamental experiments in quantum chemistry, gas properties, titration experiments, and calorimetry. This version of *Virtual ChemLab* is intended to be used in conjunction with *General Chemistry: Principles and Modern Applications* 9th Edition by Petrucci, Harwood, Herring, and Madura. An ***eLaboratory*** section has been added to the end of most chapters in the 9th Edition of the textbook, which contains problems and laboratory assignments that make use of the sophisticated laboratory simulations in *Virtual ChemLab*. This workbook contains the over 80 assignment worksheets that correspond to the brief problem descriptions in the ***eLaboratory*** sections. Many of these ***eLaboratory*** problems are similar to regular problems found in the text but require the student to measure the data in the virtual laboratory instead of having it provided for them. Most assignments, however, are experiments and laboratory work that has not been previously available to general chemistry students, such as the Millikan oil-drop experiment, a Rutherford backscattering experiment, titrations, or gas experiments that test Boyle's law. A brief description of the five general chemistry laboratories available in *Virtual ChemLab* is given below.

The general features of the inorganic simulation include 26 cations that can be added to test tubes in any combination, 11 reagents that can be added to the test tubes in any sequence and any number of times, necessary laboratory manipulations, a lab book for recording results and observations, and a stockroom for creating test tubes with known mixtures and generating practice unknowns. The simulation uses over 2,500 actual photographs to show the results of reactions and over 220 videos to show the different flame tests. With 26 cations that can be combined in any order or combination and 11 reagents that can be added in any order, there are in excess of 10^{16} possible outcomes in the simulation.

The purpose of the quantum laboratory is to allow students to explore and better understand the foundational experiments that led to the development of quantum mechanics. Because of the very sophisticated nature of most of these experiments, the quantum laboratory is the most "virtual" of the *Virtual ChemLab* laboratory simulations. In general, the laboratory consists of an optics table where a source, sample, modifier, and detector combination can be placed to perform different experiments. These devices are located in the stockroom and can be taken out of the stockroom and placed in various locations on the optics table. The emphasis here is to teach students to probe a sample (e.g., a gas, metal foil, two-slit screen, etc.) with a source (e.g., a laser, electron gun, alpha-particle source, etc.) and to detect the outcome with a specific detector (e.g., a phosphor screen, spectrometer, etc.). Heat, electric fields, or magnetic fields can also be applied to modify an aspect of the experiment.

The gas experiments included in the *Virtual ChemLab* simulated laboratory allow students to explore and better understand the behavior of ideal gases, real gases, and van der Waals gases (a model real gas). The gases laboratory contains four experiments each of which includes the four variables used to describe a gas: pressure (P), temperature (T), volume (V), and the number of moles (n). The four experiments differ by allowing one of these variables to be the dependent variable while the others are independent. The four experiments include (1) V as a function of P, T, and n using a balloon to reflect the volume changes; (2) P as a function of V, T, and n using a motor driven piston; (3) T as a function of P, V, and n again using a motor driven piston; and (4) V as a function of P, T, and n but this time using a frictionless, massless piston to reflect volume changes and using weights to apply pressure. The gases that can be used in these experiments include an ideal gas; a van der Waals gas whose parameters can be changed to represent any real gas; real gases including N_2, CO_2, CH_4, H_2O, NH_3, and He; and eight ideal gases with different molecular weights that can be added to the experiments to form gas mixtures.

The virtual titration laboratory allows students to perform precise, quantitative titrations involving acid-base and electrochemical reactions. The available laboratory equipment consists of a 50 mL buret, 5, 10, and 25 mL pipets, graduated cylinders, beakers, a stir plate, a set of 8 acid-base indicators, a pH meter/voltmeter, a conductivity meter, and an analytical balance for weighing out solids. Acid-base titrations can be performed on any combination of mono-, di-, and tri-protic acids and mono-, di-, and tri-basic bases. The pH of these titrations can be monitored using a pH meter, an indicator, and a conductivity meter as a function of volume, and this data can be saved to an electronic lab book for later analysis. A smaller set of potentiometric titrations can also be performed. Systematic and random errors in the mass and volume measurements have been included in the simulation by introducing buoyancy errors in the mass weighings, volumetric errors in the glassware, and characteristic systematic and random errors in the pH/voltmeter and conductivity meter output. These errors can be ignored, which will produce results and errors typically found in high school or freshman-level laboratory work, or the buoyancy and volumetric errors can be measured and included in the calculations to produce results better than 0.1% in accuracy and reproducibility.

The calorimetry laboratory provides students with three different calorimeters that allow them to measure various thermodynamic processes including heats of combustion, heats of solution, heats of reaction, the heat capacity, and the heat of fusion of ice. The calorimeters provided in the simulations are a classic "coffee cup" calorimeter, a dewar flask (a better version of a coffee cup), and a bomb calorimeter. The calorimetric method used in each calorimeter is based on measuring the temperature change associated with the different thermodynamic processes. Students can choose from a wide selection of organic materials to measure the heats of combustion; salts to measure the heats of solution; acids, bases, oxidants, and reductants to measure the heats of reaction; metals and alloys to measure heat capacity; and ice to measure the melting process. Temperature versus time data can be graphed during the measurements and saved to the electronic lab book for later analysis. Systematic and random errors in the mass and volume measurements have been included in the simulation by introducing buoyancy errors in the mass weighings, volumetric errors in the glassware, and characteristic systematic and random errors in the thermometer measurements.

Getting Started

A CD containing *Virtual ChemLab* is included with each copy of the 9th Edition of Petrucci/Harwood/Herring/Madura. *Virtual ChemLab* can be run off the CD or, for better speed and usability, the entire contents of the CD (about 600 MB) can be copied to the hard drive. When running *Virtual ChemLab* from the CD, first insert the CD into your CD-ROM drive and open the contents of the CD using My Computer on Windows machines or by double-clicking on the CD icon in Finder on Macintosh machines. When running from the hard drive, find where you have copied the CD contents and open the folder. To launch the simulations, double click on the *Virtual ChemLab* application (VCL) on the CD or in the folder where the CD contents have been copied.

After the program startup, students will be brought to a hallway containing three doors and a workbook sitting on a table (see Figure 1). Clicking on the electronic workbook opens and zooms into the workbook pages (see Figure 2) where students can select preset assignments that correspond to the assignments in the workbook. The *Previous* and *Next* buttons are used to page through the set of assignments, and the different assignments can also be accessed by clicking on the section titles located on

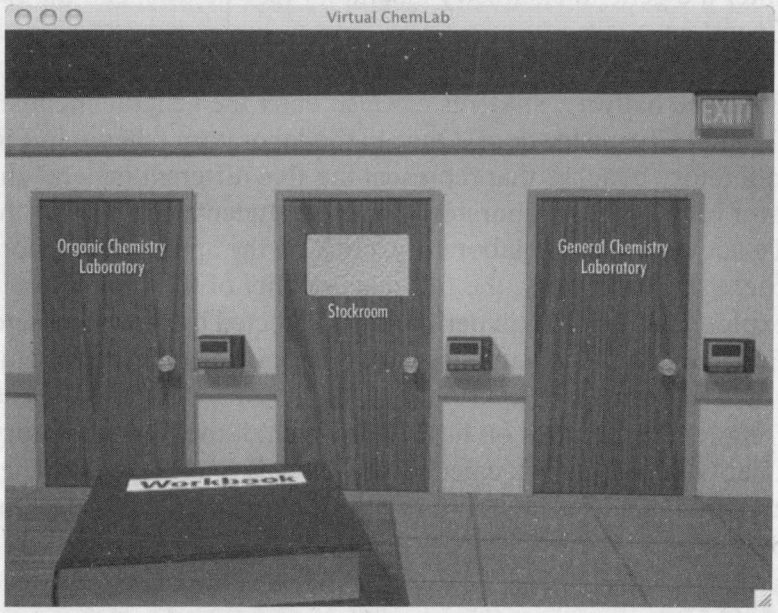

Figure 1. The "hallway" leading into the different virtual rooms in *Virtual ChemLab*. The general chemistry laboratory can be accessed by clicking on the General Chemistry door and the electronic workbook is accessed by clicking on the workbook.

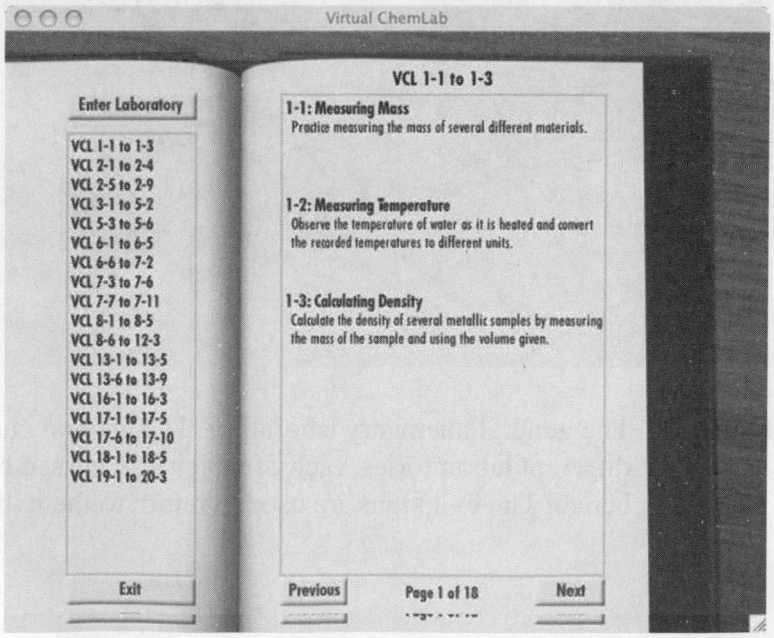

Figure 2. The electronic workbook. Preset laboratories corresponding to assignments in the workbook are accessed by clicking on the assignment.

the left page of the workbook. Clicking on the *Enter Laboratory* button will allow the students to enter the general chemistry laboratory (see below), and the *Exit* button is used to leave *Virtual ChemLab*.

From the hallway, students can also enter the general chemistry laboratory by clicking on the General Chemistry door. Once in the laboratory (shown in Figure 3), students will find five laboratory benches that represent the five different general chemistry laboratories. By mousing over each of these laboratory benches, students can display the name of the selected laboratory. To access a specific laboratory, click on the appropriate laboratory bench. While in the general chemistry laboratory, the full functionality of the simulation is available, and students are free to explore and perform experiments as directed by their instructors or by their own curiosity. The Exit signs in the general chemistry laboratory are used to return to the hallway.

Detailed instructions on how to use each of the five laboratory simulations can be found in the User Guides Folder located on the *Virtual ChemLab* CD. These same user guides can also be accessed inside each laboratory by clicking on the Pull-Down TV and clicking on the *Help* button.

Figure 3. The general chemistry laboratory. The general chemistry laboratory contains five different laboratories, each of which is accessed by clicking on the appropriate lab bench. The exit signs are used to return to the hallway.

System Requirements

Minimum system requirements are as follows:

PC
Pentium 500 MHz (Pentium II or better recommended)
128 MB RAM (256+ MB Recommended)
CD-ROM drive
600 MB of free disk space (if copying the CD contents to the hard drive)
Display capable of **and** set to millions of colors (24 bit color)
Minimum resolution 800 x 600 (1024 x 768 or higher strongly recommended)
Windows 98, Windows 2000 Professional, or Windows XP
QuickTime 5.x/6.x/7.x

Macintosh
PowerPC (G3 or better recommended)
128 MB RAM (256+ MB recommended)
CD-ROM drive
600 MB of free disk space (if copying the CD contents to the hard drive)
Display capable of **and** set to millions of colors (24-bit color)
Recommended minimum resolution 832 x 624 (1024 x 768 or higher strongly recommended)
OS X (any version)
QuickTime 5.x/6.x/7.x

Note: The above requirements are the recommended minimum hardware and system software requirements for reasonable execution speeds and reliability. However, it should be noted that the software has been successfully installed and used on computers with significantly lower capabilities than the recommendations given above with corresponding reductions in execution speed and media access time.

Installing *Virtual ChemLab*

No installation is required. This version of *Virtual ChemLab* is designed run from the CD. However, for better execution speed and usability, the entire contents of the CD can be copied to a folder on the hard drive. 600 MB of free space is required.

Important Usage Notes and Issues

1. The graphics used in the simulations require the monitor to be set to 24-bit true color (millions of colors). Lower color resolutions can be used, but the graphics will not be as sharp.

2. QuickTime 5.x or later is required for the software to run properly. The most recent version of QuickTime can be obtained at http://www.apple.com/quicktime/

3. When the simulation software has been installed on a Windows 2000 Professional operating system, there is better performance and better system stability when the Windows 2000 Support Pack 2 has been installed.

4. For unknown reasons, on some machines the QuickTime videos will not play properly if the system QuickTime settings are in their default state. This can be corrected by changing the Video Settings in QuickTime to Normal Mode.

VCL 1-1: Measuring Mass

The ability to measure the mass of a sample is an important part of many laboratory experiments. In this assignment, you will learn the important fundamentals of using an analytical balance by measuring the mass of various types of samples.

1. Start *Virtual ChemLab* and select *Measuring Mass* from the list of assignments. The lab will open in the Calorimetry laboratory.

2. Enter the stockroom by clicking inside the *Stockroom* window. Once inside the stockroom, click on the *Metals* cabinet and then open the first drawer by clicking on it. (Be patient, it may take awhile to open the drawer the first time.) When you open the drawer, a Petri dish will appear on the counter next to the cabinet. Place the sample of gold (Au) found in the drawer into the sample dish by double-clicking on the sample or by clicking and dragging it to the dish. Return to the stockroom view by clicking on the green *Zoom Out* arrow. Place the Petri dish on the stockroom counter by double-clicking on it or by clicking and dragging it to the counter. Click on the *Return to Lab* arrow to return to the laboratory.

3. Drag the Petri dish to the spotlight near the balance. Click on the *Balance* area to zoom in. Drag a piece of weighing paper to the balance pan. Record the mass of the weighing paper in the Data Table. Drag the gold sample to the balance pan and record the mass in the Data Table. Find the mass of the sample by subtracting the mass of the weighing paper from the mass of the weighing paper plus the sample. Record the mass of the gold in the Data Table.

4. Remove the gold sample from the balance and place it back on the Petri dish. With the weighing paper on the balance, click on the *Tare* button to tare or zero out the balance. The balance should read 0.0000 g. Now drag the gold sample to the balance pan and record the mass in the Data Table. You have now measured the mass of a sample by difference and by taring the balance. These are both acceptable techniques for measuring the mass of a sample.

5. Click the red disposal bucket to clean up the laboratory. Enter the stockroom by clicking inside the *Stockroom* window. Once inside the stockroom, click on the sodium chloride (NaCl) bottle located on the *Salts* shelf and drag it to the stockroom counter. You can also double click on the bottle to move it to the counter, while the left and right blue arrow keys can be used to see additional bottles. *Click on the Return* to Lab arrow to return to the laboratory.

6. Drag the bottle to the spotlight near the balance, and click on the *Balance* area to zoom in. Drag a piece of weighing paper to the balance pan and record the mass in the Data Table. Click on the bottle lid (*Remove Lid*) to remove the lid.

7. Pick up the *Scoop* and scoop out some sample by first dragging the scoop to the mouth of the bottle and then pulling the scoop down the face of the bottle. As the scoop is dragged down the face of the bottle, it will pick up different quantities of solid. Select the largest sample possible and drag the scoop to the weighing paper on the balance until it snaps in place and then let go. This will put approximately 1 g of sample on the balance. Find the mass of the sample.

8. Drag the weighing paper with the sample to the red disposal bucket. Drag a piece of weighing paper to the balance pan again and then ***Tare*** the balance so the balance reads 0.0000 g. Using the scoop, place approximately 1 g of sample on the balance and record the mass in the Data Table.

9. Repeat steps 5-8 for TNT located on the Organics shelf and record the masses in the Data Table.

Data Table

	Gold (Au)	NaCl	TNT
Mass of the weigh paper			
Mass of the weigh paper + sample			
Mass of weigh paper/sample – weigh paper			
Mass of the sample (by taring)			

10. How many significant figures are used in the final mass of the gold sample? _____

VCL 1-2: Measuring Temperature

When measuring temperature, we often use different temperature scales depending on where we live and what we are doing, and it is often necessary to be able to convert between the different temperature scales. In this assignment, you will measure the temperature of an ice/water mixture and then measure the temperature of the water at several points as you heat it to its boiling point. You will then convert the temperatures you measured to the Fahrenheit and Kelvin temperature scales.

1. Start *Virtual ChemLab* and select *Measuring Temperature* from the list of assignments. The lab will open in the Calorimetry laboratory with a coffee cup calorimeter filled with an ice/water mixture on the lab bench.

2. Wait 20-30 seconds until the temperature on the thermometer is constant and record the temperature of the ice/water mixture as T_1 in the Data and Results Table.

3. Now wait until all of the ice melts and the water begins to warm. You should be able to see this in the temperature graph window. Heat the water by turning on the calorimeter heater by clicking on the red/green switch (labeled Heater) on the calorimeter control panel. Heat the water until you get to approximately 25°C and turnoff the heater. Record the temperature of the water as T_2 in the Data and Results Table.

4. Turn on the heater again and heat the water until the water begins to boil. You should be able to see steam coming out of the calorimeter. (You can click on the clock on the wall labeled *Accelerate* to accelerate the heating process.) Record the temperature of the water at its boiling point as T_3 in the Data and Results Table.

5. Now convert the temperatures you recorded for T_1, T_2, and T_3 into °F and K and record your results in the Data and Results Table.

Data and Results Table

	T_1	T_2	T_3
°C			
°F			
K			

VCL 1-3: Calculating Density

The density of a material is an important physical property since it relates the mass of a sample to its volume. In this assignment, you will calculate the density of several metallic samples by using the volume given and measuring the mass of the sample.

1. Start *Virtual ChemLab* and select *Calculating Density* from the list of assignments. The lab will open in the Calorimetry laboratory.

2. Enter the stockroom by clicking inside the *Stockroom* window. Once inside the stockroom, click on the *Metals* cabinet and then open the first drawer by clicking on it. (Be patient, it may take awhile to open the drawer the first time.) When you open the drawer, a Petri dish will appear on the counter next to the cabinet. Place the sample of gold (Au) found in the drawer into the sample dish by double-clicking on the sample or by clicking and dragging it to the dish. Return to the stockroom view by clicking on the green *Zoom Out* arrow. Place the Petri dish on the stockroom counter by double-clicking on it or by clicking and dragging it to the counter. Click on the *Return to Lab* arrow to return to the laboratory.

3. Drag the Petri dish to the spotlight near the balance. Click on the *Balance* area to zoom in. Drag a piece of weighing paper to the balance pan, ***Tare*** the balance, and then drag the gold sample to the balance pan and record the mass in the Data and Results Table.

4. The approximate volume of the metallic samples used in the laboratory is 3.00 cm^3. Using this information and the mass of the sample, calculate the density of gold. Record your answers in the Data and Results Table below.

5. Repeat this experiment for lead (Pb) and aluminum (Al).

Data and Results

Sample	Mass of Sample (g)	Density (g/cm^3)
Au		
Pb		
Al		

6. Aluminum and its alloys are the primary metal used in the construction of airplanes. Does this make sense given its density? Why? _____

_____

VCL 2-1: Thomson Cathode Ray Tube Experiment

As scientists began to examine atoms, their first discovery was that they could extract negatively charged particles from atoms. They called these particles electrons. In order to understand the nature of these particles, scientists wanted to know how much charge they carried and how much they weighed. John Joseph (J.J.) Thomson was a physics professor at the famous Cavendish Laboratory at Cambridge University. In 1897, Thomson showed that if you could measure how far a beam of electrons was bent in an electric field and in a magnetic field, you could determine the charge-to-mass ratio (q/m_e) for the particles (electrons). Knowing the charge-to-mass ratio (q/m_e) and either the charge on the electron or the mass of the electron would allow you to calculate the other. Thomson could not obtain either in his cathode ray tube experiments and had to be satisfied with just the charge-to-mass ratio.

1. Start *Virtual ChemLab* and select *Thomson Cathode Ray Tube Experiment* from the list of assignments. The lab will open in the Quantum laboratory.

2. *What source is used in this experiment?* Drag your cursor over to the source to identify it._____

   _____

   *What type of charge do electrons have?*_____

   What detector is used in this experiment? _____

3. Turn on the *Phosphor Screen* by clicking on the red/green light switch.

   What do you observe? _____

   The phosphor screen detects charged particles (such as electrons) and it glows momentarily at the positions where the particles impact the screen.

4. It may be helpful to drag the lab window down and left and the phosphor screen window up and right in order to minimize overlap. Push the ***Grid*** button on the phosphor screen, and set the *Magnetic Field* to 30 μT. (Click buttons above and below the digits in the meter to raise and lower the value. Clicking between digits moves the decimal point.)

   What happens to the spot from the electron gun on the phosphor screen? _____

   _____

5. Set the *Magnetic Field* back to zero and set the *Electric Field* to 10 V.

   *What happens to the spot on the phosphor screen?*_____

   Where should the signal on the phosphor screen be if the electric and magnetic forces are balanced?

   _____

6. Increase the voltage of the *Electric Field* so the spot is 5 cm left of center.

   *What voltage is required?*_____

7. Increase the magnetic field strength until the spot reaches the center of the screen.

What magnetic field creates a magnetic force that balances the electric force? _____

Summarize your data.

deflected distance (d)	electric field (V)	magnetic field (B)

8. In a simplified and reduced form, the charge-to-mass ratio (q/m_e) can be calculated as follows:

$$q/m_e = \left(5.0826 \times 10^{12}\right) \cdot V \cdot d / B^2$$

where V = the electric field in volts, d = the deflected distance from center in cm after applying just the voltage, and B = magnetic field in μT.

What is your calculated value for the charge-to-mass ratio for an electron (q/m_e)? _____

_____

The modern accepted value is 1.76×10^{11}.

Calculate your percent error as follows:

$$\%\ Error = \frac{|your\ value - accepted\ value|}{accepted\ value} \times 100$$

$\%\ Error =$ _____

9. You may want to repeat the experiment several times using different size deflections.

VCL 2-2: Millikan Oil Drop Experiment

In the Thomson Cathode Ray Tube Experiment, it was discovered that you can use the deflection of an electron beam in an electric and magnetic field to measure the charge-to-mass ratio (q/m_e) of an electron. If you then want to know either the charge or the mass of an electron, you need to have a way of measuring one or the other independently. In 1909, Robert Millikan and his graduate student Harvey Fletcher showed that they could make very small oil drops and deposit electrons on these drops (1 to 10 electrons per drop). They would then measure the total charge on the oil drops by deflecting the drops with an electric field. You will get a chance to repeat their experiments and, using the results from the Thomson assignment, be able to experimentally calculate the mass of an electron.

1. Start *Virtual ChemLab* and select *Millikan Oil Drop Experiment* from the list of assignments. The lab will open in the Quantum laboratory.

2. *What is the purpose of the electron gun in this experiment?* _____

   _____

   How does this source affect the oil droplets in the oil mist chamber? _____

   _____

3. The detector in this experiment is a video camera with a microscopic eyepiece attached to view the oil droplets. Click the ***On/Off*** switch (red/green light) to turn the video camera on.

   What do you observe on the video camera screen? _____

   _____

   Do all the oil drops fall at the same speed? _____

   What force causes the drops to fall? _____

   The oil drops fall at their terminal velocity, which is the maximum velocity possible due to frictional forces such as air resistance. The terminal velocity is a function of the radius of the drop. By measuring the terminal velocity (v_t) of a droplet, the radius (r) can be calculated. Then the mass (m) of the drop can be calculated from its radius and the density of the oil. Knowing the mass of the oil droplet will allow you to calculate the charge (q) on the droplet.

   IMPORTANT: Read instructions 4 and 5 before beginning the procedure for 5.

4. *Measure the terminal velocity of a drop.* Identify a small drop near the top of the window that is falling near the center scale and click the ***Slow Motion*** button on the video camera. Wait until the drop is at a tick mark and start the timer. Let the drop fall for at least two or more tick marks and stop the timer. Do not let the drop fall off the end of the viewing scope. Each tick mark is 0.125 mm. Record the distance and the time in the data table on the following page.

5. *Measure the voltage required to stop the fall of the drop.* Having measured the terminal velocity, you now need to stop the fall of the drop by applying an electric field between the two voltage plates. This is done by clicking on the buttons on the top or bottom of the *Electric Field* until the voltage is adjusted such that the drop stops falling. This should be done while in slow motion. When the drop appears to stop, turn the slow motion off and do some final adjustments until the drop has not moved for at least one minute. Record the voltage, V, indicated on the voltage controller.

Complete the experiment for three drops and record your measurements in the data table.

Data Table

Drop	Voltage (V, in volts)	Time (t, in seconds)	Distance (d, in meters)
1			
2			
3			

The *Millikan Oil Drop Experiment* is a classic due to the simplicity of the experimental apparatus and the completeness of the data analysis. The following calculations have reduced very complex equations into simpler ones with several parameters combined into a single constant. Millikan and Fletcher accounted for the force of gravity, the force of the electric field, the density of the oil, the viscosity of the air, the viscosity of the oil, and the air pressure.

6. *Calculate the terminal velocity and record the value.* Calculate the terminal velocity, v_t, in units of $m \cdot s^{-1}$ using this equation:

$v_t = \frac{d}{t}$, where d is the distance the drop fell in meters and t is the elapsed time in seconds. Do not forget that the scale on the viewing scope is in mm (1000 mm = 1 m). _____

_____

Each of the equations in instructions 7-10 is shown with and without units. You will find it easier to use the equation without units for your calculations.

7. *Calculate the radius (r) of the drop and record the value.* With the terminal velocity, you can calculate the radius, in m, of the drop using this equation:

$$r = \left(9.0407 \times 10^{-5}\,\mathrm{m}^{1/2} \cdot \mathrm{s}^{1/2}\right) \cdot \sqrt{v_t} \quad = (9.0407 \times 10^{-5} \sqrt{v_t}\text{, without units})$$

_____

8. *Calculate the mass of the drop and record the value.* You can use the answer from #7 for the radius (r) to calculate the mass of the drop given the density of the oil. The final equation to calculate the mass, in kg, is

$$m = V_{oil} \cdot \rho_{oil} = 4\pi/3 \cdot r^3 \cdot 821\,\mathrm{kg} \cdot \mathrm{m}^{-3} \quad = (3439.0 \cdot r^3\text{, without units})$$
$$= \left(3439.0\,\mathrm{kg} \cdot \mathrm{m}^{-3}\right) \cdot r^3$$

_____

9. Since you applied a voltage across the *Electric Field* to stop the fall of the oil drop, the forces being exerted on the drop must be balanced; that is, the force due to gravity must be the same as the force due to the electric field acting on the electrons stuck to the drop: $qE = mg$.

   Calculate the total charge (Q_{tot}) on the oil drop due to the electrons using the equation:

   $$Q_{tot} = Q(n) \cdot e = \left(9.810 \times 10^{-2}\,\mathrm{C} \cdot \mathrm{kg}^{-1} \cdot \mathrm{J}^{-1}\right) \cdot m/V \quad = (9.81 \times 10^{-2}\ m/V, \text{ without units})$$

   where $Q(n)$ is the number of electrons on the drop, e is the fundamental electric charge of an electron, m is the mass calculated in #8, and V is the voltage.

   This answer will provide the total charge on the drop (Q_{tot}). The fundamental electric charge of an electron (e) is 1.6×10^{-19} C (coulombs). Divide your total charge (Q_{tot}) by e and round your answer to the nearest whole number. This is the number of electrons ($Q(n)$) that adhered to your drop. Now divide your total charge (Q_{tot}) by $Q(n)$ and you will obtain your experimental value for the charge on one electron.

10. Complete the experiment and calculations for at <u>least</u> three drops and summarize your results in the results table.

Results Table

Drop #	Terminal Velocity (v_t, in m/s)	Radius (r, in meters)	Mass (m, in kg)	Total charge on drop (Q_{tot}, in Coulombs)	Charge on one electron (C)
1					
2					
3					

11. Average your results for the charge on one electron. Calculate the percent error by:

    $$\%\ Error = \frac{\left|\text{your answer} - 1.6 \times 10^{-19}\right|}{1.6 \times 10^{-19}} \times 100\%$$

    What is your average charge for an electron? _____

    _____

    What is your percent error? _____

12. You will recall that in the Thomson experiment you were able to calculate the charge-to-mass ratio (q/m_e) as 1.7×10^{11}. Using this value for q/m_e and your average charge on an electron, calculate the mass of an electron in kg.

What is your calculated value for the mass of an electron in kg? _____

_____

VCL 2-3: Investigating the Properties of Alpha and Beta Particles

As scientists began investigating the properties of atoms, their first discovery was that they could extract negatively charged particles. They called these particles electrons, but they are also known as beta particles in the context of nuclear decay. Robert Millikan used beta particles in his famous Oil Drop Experiment. Another particle ejected during nuclear decay is the alpha particle. An alpha particle is a helium nucleus, or a helium atom without its two electrons. Consequently, an alpha particle is positively charged. Ernest Rutherford used alpha particles in his Gold Foil Experiment.

1. Start *Virtual ChemLab* and select *Alpha and Beta Particles* from the list of assignments. The lab will open in the Quantum laboratory.

2. *What source is used in this experiment?* Drag your cursor over the source to identify it. _____

   What type of charge do electrons have? _____

   What detector is used in this experiment? _____

3. Turn on the *Phosphor Screen*. (Click on the green/red button.)

   What do you observe? _____

   The phosphor screen detects charged particles (such as electrons) and it glows momentarily at the positions where the particles impact the screen.

4. Drag the lab window down and left and the phosphor screen window up and right in order to minimize the overlap. Push the ***Grid*** button on the phosphor screen, and set the *Magnetic Field* to 30 μT. (Click the button above the tens place three times. If you mistakenly click between digits, it will move the decimal point. Click it to place it where it was originally and then click above the tens place.)

   What happens to the spot from the electron gun on the phosphor screen? _____

5. Click once above the tens place on the *Electric Field* meter. Observe the spot. Click a second time above the tens place on the *Electric Field.*

   What happens to the spot from the electron gun on the phosphor screen? _____

6. Zero out the *Magnetic Field* and *Electric Field* meters by clicking on the appropriate digit buttons until the spot on the phosphor screen is centered again.

7. Double-click or click and drag the electron gun to move it to the *Stockroom* counter. Enter the *Stockroom* by clicking inside the *Stockroom*. Double-click the electron gun to move it back to the shelf. Double-click on the alpha source to select it and move it to the *Stockroom* counter. Click on the green *Return to Lab* arrow to return to the lab. Drag the alpha source from the *Stockroom* counter and place it on the table where the electron gun was originally placed (the middle spot light). Click on the front of the alpha source to open the shutter.

   What appears on the phosphor screen? _____

8. Change the unit for the *Magnetic Field* from μT to mT by clicking once above the unit. Click above the hundreds place three times to set the *Magnetic Field* to 300 mT (millitesla). This magnetic field is one million times stronger than what we used for the electron gun.

   Which direction is the spot deflected when the magnetic field is increased this time? _____

   How does this compare with the direction of movement when the magnetic field was turned on for the electrons?

   _____

   _____

9. Change the unit for the *Electric Field* from V to kV by clicking once above the unit. Observe the spot as you increase the *Electric Field* strength from 0 kV to 5 kV. The movement is slight so pay careful attention.

   Which direction is the spot moved when you increase the Electric Field? _____

   How does this compare with the direction of movement for the electron beam in the Electric Field?

   _____

   Why does it take significantly stronger magnetic and electric field strengths to move the beam of alpha particles compared with the beam of electrons (beta particles)?

   _____

10. Return the values on the two meters to zero. Double-click (or click and drag) the alpha source and the phosphor screen to return them to the *Stockroom* counter. Enter the *Stockroom*. Double-click on the alpha source and the phosphor screen to place them on the shelf. Select the laser and the video camera by double-clicking on them, and then click on the green *Return to Lab* arrow to return to the lab. Place the laser in the center spotlight on the left and turn the laser on (click on the red/green light). Place the video camera on the center spotlight on the right and click the video camera to turn it on. Set the laser intensity to 1 nW and the wavelength to 20 nm. This wavelength is in the x-ray region of the electromagnetic spectrum. The purple dot is a representation of the x-rays hitting the video camera. Change the *Electric Field* and *Magnetic Field* to determine the effect on the x-rays.

    Did the electric or magnetic fields affect the x-rays? Why or why not? _____

    _____

    Summarize what you have learned about electrons (beta particles), alpha particles, and x-rays.

    _____

    _____

    _____

VCL 2-4: Rutherford's Backscattering Experiment

A key experiment in understanding the nature of atomic structure was completed by Ernest Rutherford in 1911. He set up an experiment that directed a beam of alpha particles (helium nuclei) through a gold foil and then onto a detector screen. According to the "plum-pudding" atomic model, electrons float around inside a cloud of positive charge. Based on this model, Rutherford expected that almost all of the alpha particles should pass through the gold foil and not be deflected. A few of the alpha particles would experience a slight deflection due to the attraction to the negative electrons (alpha particles have a charge of +2). Imagine his surprise when a few alpha particles deflected at all angles, even nearly straight backwards.

According to the "plum-pudding" model there was nothing in the atom massive enough to deflect the alpha particles. Rutherford's reaction was that this was ". .almost as incredible as if you fired a 15-inch shell at a piece of tissue paper and it came back and hit you." He suggested that the experimental data could only be explained if the majority of the mass of an atom was concentrated in a small, positively charged central nucleus. This experiment provided the evidence needed to prove the nuclear model of the atom. In this experiment, you will make observations similar to those of Professor Rutherford.

1. Start *Virtual ChemLab* and select *Rutherford's Backscattering Experiment* from the list of assignments. The lab will open in the Quantum laboratory.

2. The experiment will be set up on the lab table. The gray box on the left side of the table contains a sample of ^{241}Am.

   What particles are emitted from this source? _____

   What are alpha particles? _____

   _____

3. Mouse over the metal foil stand in the middle of the table.

   What metal foil is used? If you want to see the metal foil, click and hold on the metal stand. _____

4. Point the cursor to the detector (on the right).

   What detector is used in this experiment? _____

5. Turn on the detector by clicking on the red/green light switch.

   What does the signal in the middle of the screen represent? _____

   _____

   The phosphor screen detects charged particles (such as alpha particles) and it glows momentarily at the positions where the particles impact the screen.

   What other signals do you see on the phosphor detection screen? _____

   _____

What do these signals represent? _____

Click the ***Persist*** button (the dotted arrow) on the phosphor detector screen.

According to the plum pudding model, what is causing the deflection of the alpha particles?

_____

_____

Make a general observation about the number of alpha particles that hit the phosphor detection screen in a minute's worth of time.

_____

6. Now, you will make observations at different angles of deflection. Click on the main laboratory window to bring it to the front. Grab the phosphor detection screen by its base and move it to the spotlight in the top right corner. The ***Persist*** button should still be on.

   Observe the number of hits in this position as compared with the first detector position. _____

   _____

7. Move the detector to the top center spotlight position at a 90° angle to the foil stand.

   Observe the number of hits in this spotlight position as compared with the first detector position. ___

   _____

8. Move the detector to the top left spotlight position and observe the number of hits on the phosphor screen in one minute.

   Observe the number of hits in this spotlight position as compared with the first detector position. ___

   _____

What causes the alpha particles to deflect backwards? _____

How do these results disprove the plum pudding model? Keep in mind that there are 1,000,000 alpha particles passing through the gold foil per second.

_____

_____

Are the gold atoms composed mostly of matter or empty space? _____

How does the Gold Foil Experiment show that almost all of the mass of an atom is concentrated in a small positively charged central atom?

_____

_____

_____

Students often ask, "Why did Rutherford use gold foil?" The most common response is that gold is soft and malleable and can be made into very thin sheets of foil. There is another reason, which you can discover for yourself.

9. Turn off the phosphor detection screen. Double-click the base of the metal foil holder to move it to the stockroom window. (You can also click and drag it to the counter.) Click on the *Stockroom* to enter. Click on the metal sample box on the top shelf. Click on *Mg* to select magnesium. Click on the *Return to Lab* arrow.

10. Move the metal foil sample holder from the stockroom window back to the center of the table. Move the phosphor screen back to its original location on the right side of the table and turn it on. Click ***Persist***. Observe the number of hits with magnesium compared with the number of hits with a gold sample.

    Why would Rutherford choose gold foil instead of magnesium foil? Explain. _____

    _____

    _____

    _____

VCL 2-5: Counting Atoms

1. Start *Virtual ChemLab* and select *Counting Atoms and Molecules* from the list of assignments. The lab will open in the Calorimetry laboratory.

2. Enter the stockroom by clicking inside the *Stockroom* window. Once inside the stockroom, click on the *Metals* cabinet and then open the top drawer by clicking on it. When you open the drawer, a Petri dish will appear on the counter next to the cabinet. Place the sample of gold (Au) found in the drawer into the sample dish by double-clicking on the sample or by clicking and dragging it to the dish. Return to the stockroom view by clicking on the green *Zoom Out* arrow. Place the Petri dish on the stockroom counter by double-clicking on it or by clicking and dragging it to the counter. Click on the *Return to Lab* arrow to return to the laboratory.

3. Drag the Petri dish to the spotlight near the balance. Click on the *Balance* area to zoom in. Drag a piece of weighing paper to the balance pan, ***Tare*** the balance, and then drag the gold sample to the balance pan and record the mass.

   Mass =

4. *Calculate the moles of Au contained in the sample.*

5. *Calculate the atoms of Au contained in the sample.*

VCL 2-6: Counting Atoms

1. Start *Virtual ChemLab* and select *Counting Atoms and Molecules* from the list of assignments. The lab will open in the Calorimetry laboratory.

2. Enter the stockroom by clicking inside the *Stockroom* window. Once inside the stockroom, click on the *Metals* cabinet and then open the third drawer by clicking on it. When you open the drawer, a Petri dish will appear on the counter next to the cabinet. Place the sample of lead (Pb) found in the drawer into the sample dish by double-clicking on the sample or by clicking and dragging it to the dish. Return to the stockroom view by clicking on the green *Zoom Out* arrow. Place the Petri dish on the stockroom counter by double-clicking on it or by clicking and dragging it to the counter. Click on the *Return to Lab* arrow to return to the laboratory.

3. Drag the Petri dish to the spotlight near the balance. Click on the *Balance* area to zoom in. Drag a piece of weighing paper to the balance pan, ***Tare*** the balance, and then drag the lead sample to the balance pan and record the mass.

   Mass =

4. *Calculate the moles of Pb contained in the sample.*

5. *Calculate the atoms of Pb contained in the sample.*

6. Repeat steps 2-5 for uranium. Record the mass, the moles, and the atoms of uranium.

   Mass of uranium =
   Moles of uranium =
   Atoms of uranium =

VCL 2-7: Counting Atoms

1. Start *Virtual ChemLab* and select *Counting Atoms and Molecules* from the list of assignments. The lab will open in the Calorimetry laboratory.

2. Enter the stockroom by clicking inside the *Stockroom* window. Once inside the stockroom, click on the *Metals* cabinet and then open the first drawer by clicking on it. When you open the drawer, a Petri dish will appear on the counter next to the cabinet. Place the sample of erbium (Er) found in the drawer into the sample dish by double-clicking on the sample or by clicking and dragging it to the dish. Return to the stockroom view by clicking on the green *Zoom Out* arrow. Place the Petri dish on the stockroom counter by double-clicking on it or by clicking and dragging it to the counter. Click on the *Return to Lab* arrow to return to the laboratory.

3. Drag the Petri dish to the spotlight near the balance. Click on the *Balance* area to zoom in. Drag a piece of weighing paper to the balance pan, ***Tare*** the balance, and then drag the erbium sample to the balance pan and record the mass in the data and results table.

4. *Calculate the moles and the atoms of erbium and enter the results in the data and results table below.*

5. Repeat steps 2-4 for sodium, tungsten, and a metal of your choice.

Data and Results Table

	erbium (Er)	sodium (Na)	tungsten (W)	your choice
Mass (grams)				
Molar Mass (g/mol)				
Moles of each element				
Atoms of each element				

VCL 2-8: Counting Protons, Neutrons, and Electrons

1. Start *Virtual ChemLab* and select *Counting Protons, Neutrons, and Electrons* from the list of assignments. The lab will open in the Calorimetry laboratory.

2. Enter the stockroom by clicking inside the *Stockroom* window. Once inside the stockroom, click on the *Metals* cabinet and then open the third drawer by clicking on it. When you open the drawer, a Petri dish will appear on the counter next to the cabinet. Place the sample of scandium (Sc) found in the drawer into the sample dish by double-clicking on the sample or by clicking and dragging it to the dish. Return to the stockroom view by clicking on the green *Zoom Out* arrow. Place the Petri dish on the stockroom counter by double-clicking on it or by clicking and dragging it to the counter. Click on the *Return to Lab* arrow to return to the laboratory.

3. Drag the Petri dish to the spotlight near the balance. Click on the *Balance* area to zoom in. Drag a piece of weighing paper to the balance pan, ***Tare*** the balance and drag the scandium sample to the balance pan.

   Record the mass of the sample. _____

4. *Calculate the moles of Sc contained in the sample.*

5. *Calculate the atoms of Sc contained in the sample.*

6. ^{45}Sc is the only naturally occurring isotope of scandium.

   How many protons, neutrons and electrons are there in one atom of ^{45}Sc? _____

   _____

7. *Calculate the number of protons, neutrons, and electrons in the sample of scandium that you weighed if it is 100% ^{45}Sc.*

VCL 2-9: Counting Protons, Neutrons, and Electrons

1. Start *Virtual ChemLab* and select *Counting Protons, Neutrons, and Electrons* from the list of assignments. The lab will open in the Calorimetry laboratory.

2. Enter the stockroom by clicking inside the *Stockroom* window. Once inside the stockroom, click on the *Metals* cabinet and then open the top drawer by clicking on it. When you open the drawer, a Petri dish will appear on the counter next to the cabinet. Place the sample of bismuth (Bi) found in the drawer into the sample dish by double-clicking on the sample or by clicking and dragging it to the dish. Return to the stockroom view by clicking on the green *Zoom Out* arrow. Place the Petri dish on the stockroom counter by double-clicking on it or by clicking and dragging it to the counter. Click on the *Return to Lab* arrow to return to the laboratory.

3. Drag the Petri dish to the spotlight near the balance. Click on the *Balance* area to zoom in. Drag a piece of weighing paper to the balance pan, ***Tare*** the balance and drag the bismuth sample to the balance pan.

   Record the mass of the sample. _____

4. *Calculate the moles of Bi contained in the sample.*

5. *Calculate the atoms of Bi contained in the sample.*

6. ^{209}Bi is the only naturally occurring isotope of bismuth.

   How many protons, neutrons and electrons are there in one atom of ^{209}Bi*?* _____

   _____

7. *How many protons, neutrons and electrons are there in one ion of* $^{209}Bi^{5+}$*?* _____

   _____

8. *Calculate the number of protons, neutrons, and electrons in a sample of* $^{209}Bi^{5+}$ *that has the same mass as the bismuth sample you weighed.*

VCL 3-1: Counting Molecules

1. Start *Virtual ChemLab* and select *Counting Atoms and Molecules* from the list of assignments. The lab will open in the Calorimetry laboratory.

2. Enter the stockroom by clicking inside the *Stockroom* window. Once inside the stockroom, click on the sodium chloride (NaCl) bottle located on the Salts shelf and drag it to the stockroom counter. You can also double click on the bottle to move it to the counter, while the left and right blue arrow keys can be used to see additional bottles. Click on the *Return to Lab* arrow to return to the laboratory.

3. Drag the bottle to the spotlight near the balance, and click on the *Balance* area to zoom in. Drag a piece of weighing paper to the balance pan and then ***Tare*** the balance so the balance reads 0.0000 g. Click on the bottle lid (*Remove Lid*) to remove the lid.

4. Pick up the *Scoop* and scoop out some sample by first dragging the scoop to the mouth of the bottle and then pulling the scoop down the face of the bottle. As the scoop is dragged down the face of the bottle it will pick up different quantities of solid. Select the largest sample possible and drag the scoop to the weighing paper on the balance until it snaps in place and then let go. This will put approximately 1 g of sample on the balance.

   Record the mass of the sample. _____

5. *Calculate the moles of NaCl contained in the sample.*

6. *Calculate the moles of each element in NaCl.* _____

7. *Calculate the number of atoms for each element in NaCl.* _____

   _____

VCL 3-2: Counting Molecules

1. Start *Virtual ChemLab* and select *Counting Atoms and Molecules* from the list of assignments. The lab will open in the Calorimetry laboratory.

2. Enter the stockroom by clicking inside the *Stockroom* window. Once inside the stockroom, click on the bottle containing table sugar (sucrose, $C_{12}H_{22}O_{11}$) located on the Organics shelf and drag it to the stockroom counter. You can also double click on the bottle to move it to the counter, while the left and right blue arrow keys can be used to see additional bottles. Click on the *Return to Lab* arrow to return to the laboratory.

3. Drag the bottle to the spotlight near the balance, and click on the *Balance* area to zoom in. Drag a piece of weighing paper to the balance pan and then ***Tare*** the balance so the balance reads 0.0000 g. Click on the bottle lid (*Remove Lid*) to remove the lid.

4. Pick up the *Scoop* and scoop out some sample by first dragging the scoop to the mouth of the bottle and then pulling the scoop down the face of the bottle. As the scoop is dragged down the face of the bottle it will pick up different quantities of solid. Select the largest sample possible and drag the scoop to the weighing paper on the balance until it snaps in place and then let go. This will put approximately 1 g of sample on the balance. Record the mass of the sample in the data and results table on the following page.

5. Repeat steps 2-4 for NH_4Cl (ammonium chloride) located on the Salts shelf and record the mass in the Data and Results Table.

6. *Calculate the moles of $C_{12}H_{22}O_{11}$ contained in the first sample and record your results in the data and results table.*

7. *Calculate the moles of each element in $C_{12}H_{22}O_{11}$ and record your results in the data and results table.*

8. *Calculate the number of atoms of each element in $C_{12}H_{22}O_{11}$ and record your results in the data and results table.*

9. Repeat steps 6-8 for NH_4Cl and record your results in the data and results table.

10. *Which of the compounds contains the most total number of atoms?* _____

Data and Results Table

	$C_{12}H_{22}O_{11}$	NH_4Cl
Mass (grams)		
Molar Mass (g/mol)		
Moles of compound		
Moles of each element		
Atoms of each element		

VCL 3-3: Names and Formulas of Ionic Compounds

In this problem, you will go into the virtual laboratory and make a series of ionic compounds containing the cations Ag^+, Pb^+, Ca^{2+}, Fe^{3+}, and Cu^{2+}; observe the reactions and identify the color of the compound formed; write the chemical formulas; and write the chemical name.

1. Start *Virtual ChemLab* and select *Names and Formulas of Ionic Compounds* from the list of assignments. The lab will open in the Inorganic laboratory.

2. Enter the stockroom by clicking inside the *Stockroom* window. Once inside the stockroom, drag a test tube from the box and place it on the metal test tube stand. You can then click on the bottle of Ag^+ ion solution on the shelf to add it to the test tube. Click ***Done*** to send the test tube back to the lab. Click on the *Return to Lab* arrow.

3. Place the test tube containing the Ag^+ solution in the metal test tube stand. Click on the ***Divide*** button on the bottom (with the large red arrow) four times to make four additional test tubes containing Ag^+. With one test tube in the metal stand and four others in the blue rack, click on the Na_2S bottle located on the lab bench. You will be able to observe what happens in the window at the bottom left. Record your observation in the table on the following page and write a correct chemical formula and name for the product of the reaction. If the solution remains clear, record NR, for no reaction. Drag this test tube to the red disposal bucket on the right.

4. Place a second tube from the blue rack (containing Ag^+) on the metal stand. Add Na_2SO_4. Record your observations and discard the tube. Use the next tube but add *NaCl*, and record your observations. Use the next tube but add *NaOH*, and record your observations. With the last tube add Na_2CO_3 and record your observations. When you are completely finished, click on the red disposal bucket to clear the lab.

5. Return to the stockroom and repeat steps 2-4 for Pb^{2+}, Ca^{2+}, Fe^{3+}, and Cu^{2+}. Complete the table on the following page.

   Each cell should include a description of what you observed when the reagents were mixed and a correct chemical formula and name for all solutions that turned cloudy and NR for all solutions that did not react or remained clear. Remember to include roman numerals where appropriate.

	Ag^{+}	Pb^{2+}	Ca^{2+}	Fe^{3+}	Cu^{2+}
Na_2S (S^{2-})					
Na_2SO_4 (SO_4^{2-})					
NaCl (Cl^{-})					
NaOH (OH^{-})					
Na_2CO_3 (CO_3^{2-})					

VCL 5-1: Strong and Weak Electrolytes

1. Start *Virtual ChemLab* and select *Strong and Weak Electrolytes* from the list of assignments. The lab will open in the Titration laboratory.

2. Enter the stockroom by clicking inside the *Stockroom* window. Once inside the stockroom, double-click or click and drag on the three reagents, *NaCl*, Na_2CO_3 (100%), and $NaHCO_3$ (100%) to move them to the stockroom counter. Click on the green *Return To Lab* arrow to return to the laboratory.

3. For each salt that was selected in the stockroom, complete the following procedure: double-click or click and drag the bottle on the stockroom counter to move it to the spotlight next to the balance. Click on the *Beakers* drawer and place a beaker in the spotlight next to the salt bottle in the balance area. Click on the *Balance* area to zoom in and open the bottle by clicking on the lid (*Remove Lid*). Drag a piece of weighing paper and drop it on the balance and then ***Tare*** the balance. Pick up the *Scoop* and scoop out some sample by first dragging the scoop to the mouth of the bottle and then pulling the scoop down the face of the bottle. As the scoop is dragged down the face of the bottle it will pick up different quantities of solid. Select the largest sample possible and drag the scoop to the balance and drop it on the weighing paper. This will put approximately 1 g of sample on the balance. Now drag the weighing paper with the sample and drop it in the beaker. Click on the green *Zoom Out* arrow to return to the laboratory.

   Move the beaker to the stir plate. Pick up the 25 mL graduated cylinder near the sink and hold it under the water tap until it fills. Pour the water into the beaker by dragging and dropping the cylinder on the beaker. Turn on the conductivity meter located on the lower right of the table and place the conductivity probe in the beaker and record the conductivity of the solution in the data table below. Double-click on the salt bottle to place it back on the stockroom counter. Place the beaker in the red disposal bucket. Repeat for the other two reagents.

4. When you have completed the three reagents, return to the *Stockroom*. Double-click on each bottle to return it to the shelf. Obtain three more samples (two salts and one solution): KNO_3, NH_4Cl, and NH_3 and return to the laboratory. Follow procedure #3 for NH_4Cl, and KNO_3.

   For the NH_3 solution, complete the following procedure: Place a beaker on the stir plate. Pick up the NH_3 solution from the stockroom shelf, drag it to the 25 mL graduated cylinder, and let go to fill the cylinder. The solution bottle will automatically go back to the stockroom shelf. Drag the 25 mL graduated cylinder to the beaker on the stir plate and drop it to transfer the solution into the beaker. Place the conductivity meter probe in the beaker and record the conductivity in the data table.

5. When you have completed the three reagents, return to the *Stockroom*. Double-click on each bottle to return it to the shelf. Obtain two more samples: *HCl* and *HCN*. Measure the conductivity of each solution following procedure #4 and record the conductivity in the data table.

Data Table

NaCl	Na_2CO_3	$NaHCO_3$	KNO_3
NH_4Cl	NH_3	HCl	HCN

6. Electrolytes are compounds that conduct electricity in aqueous solutions. *Which compounds in your table are electrolytes? Which are not electrolytes?* _____

_____

7. *Would any of these electrolytes conduct electricity in the solid form? Explain.* _____

_____

8. *Are these ionic or covalent compounds? Classify each compound in the grid as ionic or covalent. For a compound to be an electrolyte, what must happen when it dissolves in water?* _____

_____

_____

9. When an ionic solid dissolves in water, water molecules attract the ions causing them to dissociate or come apart. The resulting dissolved ions are electrically charged particles that allow the solution to conduct electricity. The following chemical equations represent this phenomenon:

$$NaCl\,(s) = Na^{+}\,(aq) + Cl^{-}\,(aq)$$
$$Na_2CO_3\,(s) = 2Na^{+}\,(aq) + CO_3^{2-}\,(aq)$$

Write a similar balanced chemical equation for each electrolyte in the data table.

10. *After examining the chemical reactions for the electrolytes, why does Na_2CO_3 have a higher conductivity than all of the other electrolytes?* _____

_____

_____

VCL 5-2: Writing Balanced Precipitation Reactions

In this problem, you will go into the virtual laboratory and perform a series of precipitation reactions using Ag^+, Pb^{2+}, and Sb^{3+}. After observing the reactions, you will write the net ionic equations representing these reactions and then balance them.

1. Start *Virtual ChemLab* and select *Writing Balanced Precipitation Reactions* from the list of assignments. The lab will open in the Inorganic laboratory.

2. Enter the stockroom by clicking inside the *Stockroom* window. Once inside the stockroom, drag a test tube from the box and place it on the metal test tube stand. You can then click on the bottle of Ag^+ ion solution (it is $AgNO_3$) on the shelf to add it to the test tube. Click ***Done*** to send the test tube back to the lab. Repeat for Pb^{2+} ($Pb(NO_3)_2$ and Sb^{3+} ($Sb(OH)_3$). Click on the *Return to Lab* arrow.

3. Click on the handle at the bottom of the TV monitor. Moving your mouse over each test tube in the test-tube rack will allow you to identify it on the TV monitor. You can also click on the label at the top of each test tube in order to label the test tubes. Place the test tube containing the Ag^+ solution in the metal test tube stand. You will be able to observe what happens in the window at the bottom left. Click on the Na_2CO_3 reagent bottle to add it to the test tube in the stand.

   What color is the precipitate? Write a correct balanced net ionic equation for the reaction.

   _____

   When you have finished writing the equation and making your observations, place the test tube containing the precipitate in the red disposal bucket.

4. Place the test tube containing the Pb^{2+} solution in the metal test tube stand. Click on the *NaCl* reagent bottle to add it to the test tube in the stand.

   What color is the precipitate? Write a correct balanced net ionic equation for this reaction.

   _____

   When you have finished writing the equation and making your observations, place the test tube containing the precipitate in the red disposal bucket.

5. Place the test tube containing the Sb^{3+} solution in the metal test tube stand. Note that the antimony is not soluble and you will have a double displacement reaction. Click on the Na_2S reagent bottle to add it to the test tube in the stand.

   What color is the precipitate? Write a correct balanced net ionic equation for the reaction.

   _____

VCL 5-3: Precipitation Reactions

1. Start *Virtual ChemLab* and select *Precipitation Reactions* from the list of assignments. The lab will open in the Inorganic laboratory.

2. React each of the cations (across the top) with each of the anions (down the left) according to the data table using the following procedures:

Data Table

	$AgNO_3$ (Ag^+)	$Pb(NO_3)_2$ (Pb^{2+})	$Ca(NO_3)_2$ (Ca^{2+})
Na_2CO_3 (CO_3^{2-})	*a*	*f*	*k*
Na_2S (S^{2-})	*b*	*g*	*l*
NaOH (OH^-)	*c*	*h*	*m*
Na_2SO_4 (SO_4^{2-})	*d*	*i*	*n*
NaCl (Cl^-)	*e*	*j*	*o*

a. Enter the stockroom by clicking inside the *Stockroom* window. Once inside the stockroom, drag a test tube from the box and place it on the metal test tube stand. You can then click on the bottle of Ag^+ ion solution on the shelf to add it to the test tube. Click ***Done*** to send the test tube back to the lab. Click on the *Return to Lab* arrow.

b. Place the test tube containing the Ag^+ solution in the metal test tube stand. Click on the ***Divide*** button on the bottom (with the large red arrow) four times to make four additional test tubes containing Ag^+. With one test tube in the metal stand and four others in the blue rack, click on the Na_2CO_3 bottle on the reagent shelf and observe what happens in the window at the bottom left. Record your observation in the table above. If the solution remains clear, record NR for no reaction. Drag this test tube to the red disposal bucket on the right.

c. Drag a second tube from the blue rack to the metal stand. Add Na_2S, record your observations and discard the tube. Continue with the third, fourth and fifth tube, but add NaOH, Na_2SO_4, and NaCl respectively. Record your observations and discard the tubes. When you are finished, click on the red disposal bucket to clear the lab.

d. Return to the stockroom and repeat steps a-c for five test tubes of Pb^{2+} and Ca^{2+}. Record your observations in the data table. If no precipitate forms write NR for no reaction.

3. *What happens in grid space d? What other reactions give similar results? Is it necessary to write an equation when no reaction occurs? Explain.* _____

_____

_____

4. *Write balanced equations for all precipitation reactions you observed.*

a.

b.

c.

e.

f.

g.

i.

j.

k.

m.

5. *Write balanced net ionic equations for all precipitation reactions you observed.*

a.

b.

c.

e.

f.

g.

i.

j.

k.

m.

VCL 5-4: Concepts in Acid-Base Titrations

Titrations provide a method of quantitatively measuring the concentration of an unknown solution. In an acid-base titration, this is done by delivering a titrant of known concentration into an analyte of known volume. (The concentration of an unknown titrant can also be determined by titration with an analyte of known concentration and volume.) Titration curves (graphs of volume vs. pH) have characteristic shapes. The graph can be used to determine the strength or weakness of an acid or base. The equivalence point of the titration, or the point where the analyte has been completely consumed by the titrant, is identified by the point where the pH changes rapidly over a small volume of titrant delivered. There is a steep incline or decline at this point of the titration curve. It is also common to use an indicator that changes color at or near the equivalence point. In this assignment, you will observe this titration curve by titrating the strong acid HCl with the strong base NaOH.

1. Start *Virtual ChemLab* and select *Concepts in Acid-Base Titrations* from the list of assignments. The lab will open in the Titration laboratory.

2. Click the *Lab Book* to open it. The buret will be filled with NaOH. The horizontal position of the orange handle is off for the stopcock. Click the ***Save*** button in the *Buret Zoom View* window. Open the stopcock by pulling down on the orange handle. The vertical position delivers solution the fastest with three intermediate rates in between. Turn the stopcock to one of the fastest positions. Observe the titration curve. When the volume reaches 35 mL, double-click the stopcock to stop the titration. Click ***Stop*** in the *Buret Zoom View*. A blue data link will be created in the lab book, click on it to view the data.

3. The beaker contains 0.3000 M HCl and the buret contains 0.3000 M NaOH.

4. *Write a complete balanced equation for the neutralization reaction between HCl and NaOH.*

   _____

   The following questions can be answered by examining the *Plot and Data Viewer* windows.

5. *What was the pH and color of the solution at the beginning of the titration?* _____

6. *What was the pH and color of the solution at the end of the titration?* _____

   _____

7. Examine the graph of the pH vs. volume (blue line).

   Sketch the shape of the titration graph of pH vs. volume.

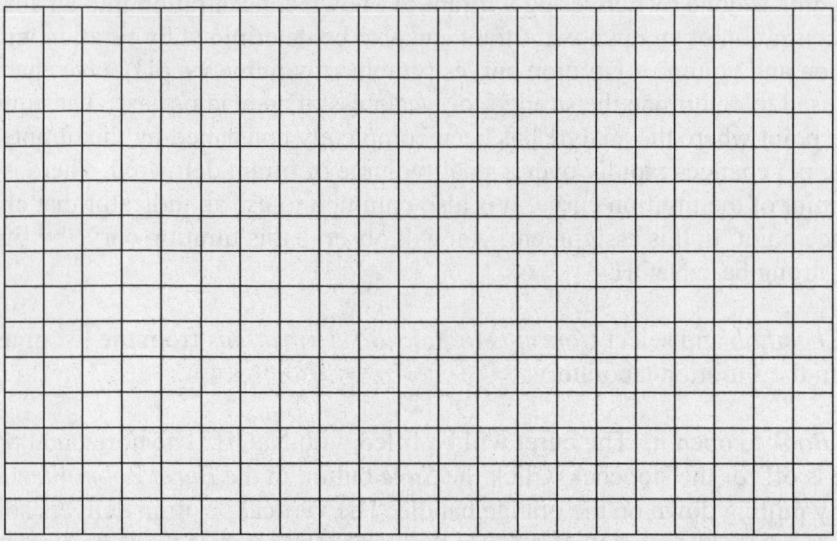

8. *What happens to the pH around 25 mL?* _____

9. *What would cause the change observed in question #4?* _____

_____

_____

_____

VCL 5-5: Acid-Base Titration: Practice

Titrations provide a method of quantitatively measuring the concentration of an unknown solution. In an acid-base titration, this is done by delivering a titrant of known concentration into an analyte of known volume. In this assignment, you will titrate a 0.3000 M solution of NaOH into 25 mL of 0.3000 M HCl. Although in this case you know the concentration of both NaOH and HCl, this will give you practice in performing a titration and calculating the concentration of the analyte, which in this case is HCl.

1. Start *Virtual ChemLab* and select *Acid-Base Titration: Practice* from the list of assignments. The lab will open in the Titrations laboratory.

2. Click the *Lab Book* to open it. Click the *Buret Zoom View* window to bring it to the front. The buret is filled with 0.3000 M NaOH. The beaker has 25.00 mL of 0.3000 M HCl. The pH meter is turned on and has been calibrated. The indicator is bromocresol green.

3. *Perform the titration*. Click the ***Save*** button in the *Buret Zoom View* window so the titration data can be saved. The horizontal position of the orange handle is off for the stopcock. Open the stopcock by pulling down on the orange handle. The vertical position delivers solution the fastest with three intermediate rates in between. Turn the stopcock to one of the fastest positions. Observe the titration curve. When the blue line in the graph window (the pH curve) begins to turn up, double-click the stopcock to turn it off. Move the stopcock down one position to add volume drop by drop.

   There are two methods for determining the volume at the equivalence point: (1) Stop the titration (close the stopcock) when a color change occurs, and then click the ***Stop*** button in the *Buret Zoom View*. A blue data link will appear in the lab book. Click the blue data link to open the *Data View* window. Scroll down to the last data entry and record the volume at the equivalence point. OR (2) Add drops slowly through the equivalence point until the pH reaches approximately 12. Click the ***Stop*** button in the *Buret Zoom View*. A blue data link will appear in the lab book. Click the blue data link to open the *Data View* window. Click ***Select All*** button to copy and paste the data to a spreadsheet program. Plot the first derivative of pH vs. volume. The peak will indicate the volume of the equivalence point since this is where the pH is changing the most rapidly as the volume changes.

4. *What volume of 0.3000 M NaOH was required by the titration to reach the equivalence point?*

   _____

5. *Calculate the molarity of the HCl using 25.00 mL of HCl solution and the volume of the 0.3000 M NaOH from your titration.*

6. *Remember that the concentration of your HCl solution is 0.3000 M. Calculate the percent error using the formula:*

$$\%\ Error = \frac{|your\ calculated\ answer - the\ actual\ answer|}{the\ predicted\ answer} \times 100$$

$$\%\ Error =$$

If you want to repeat the titration, click *Exit*, select this problem from the workbook again, and repeat the experiment.

VCL 5-6: Acid-Base Titration: Unknown HCl

Titrations provide a method of quantitatively measuring the concentration of an unknown solution. In an acid-base titration, this is done by delivering a titrant of known concentration into an analyte of known volume. In this assignment, you will titrate a 0.2564 M solution of NaOH into 25 mL of an unknown concentration of HCl and calculate the concentration of the HCl solution.

1. Start *Virtual ChemLab* and select *Acid-Base Titration: Unknown HCl* from the list of assignments. The lab will open in the Titrations laboratory.

2. Click the *Lab Book* to open it. Click the *Buret Zoom View* window to bring it to the front. The buret is filled with 0.2564 M NaOH. The beaker has 25.00 mL of unknown HCl. The pH meter is turned on and has been calibrated. The indicator is bromocresol green.

3. *Perform the titration.* Click the ***Save*** button in the *Buret Zoom View* window so the titration data can be saved. The horizontal position of the orange handle is off for the stopcock. Open the stopcock by pulling down on the orange handle. The vertical position delivers solution the fastest with three intermediate rates in between. Turn the stopcock to one of the fastest positions. Observe the titration curve. When the blue line in the graph window (the pH curve) begins to turn up, double-click the stopcock to turn it off. Move the stopcock down one position to add volume drop by drop.

   There are two methods for determining the volume at the equivalence point: (1) Stop the titration (close the stopcock) when a color change occurs, and then click the ***Stop*** button in the *Buret Zoom View*. A blue data link will appear in the lab book. Click the blue data link to open the *Data View* window. Scroll down to the last data entry and record the volume at the equivalence point. OR (2) Add drops slowly through the equivalence point until the pH reaches approximately 12. Click the ***Stop*** button in the *Buret Zoom View*. A blue data link will appear in the lab book. Click the blue data link to open the *Data View* window. Click ***Select All*** button to copy and paste the data to a spreadsheet program. Plot the first derivative of pH vs. volume. The peak will indicate the volume of the equivalence point since this is where the pH is changing the most rapidly as the volume changes.

4. *What is your unknown sample number?* _____

   _____

5. *What volume of 0.2564 M NaOH was required by the titration to reach the equivalence point?*

   _____

   _____

6. *Calculate the molarity of the HCl using 25.00 mL of HCl solution and the volume of the 0.2564 M NaOH from your titration.* _____

VCL 6-1: Boyle's Law: Pressure and Volume

Robert Boyle, a philosopher and theologian, studied the properties of gases in the 17th century. He noticed that gases behave similarly to springs; when compressed or expanded, they tend to 'spring' back to their original volume. He published his findings in 1662 in a monograph entitled *The Spring of the Air and Its Effects*. You will make observations similar to those of Robert Boyle and learn about the relationship between the pressure and volume of an ideal gas.

1. Start *Virtual ChemLab* and select *Boyle's Law: Pressure and Volume* from the list of assignments. The lab will open in the Gases laboratory.

2. Note that the balloon in the chamber is filled with 0.300 moles of an ideal gas (MW = 4 g/mol) at a temperature of 298 K, a pressure of 1.00 atm, and a volume of 7.336 L. To the left of the Pressure LCD controller is a lever that will decrease and increase the pressure as it is moved up or down; the digit changes depending on how far the lever is moved. Digits may also be clicked directly to type in the desired number. You may want to practice adjusting the lever so that you can decrease and increase the pressure accurately. Make sure the moles, temperature, and pressure are returned to their original values before proceeding.

3. Click on the *Lab Book* to open it. Back in the laboratory, click on the ***Save*** button to start recording *P, V, T,* and *n* data to the lab book. Increase the pressure from 1 atm to 10 atm one atmosphere at a time. Click ***Stop*** to stop recording data, and a blue data link will appear in the lab book. To help keep track of your data links, enter 'Ideal Gas 1' next to the link.

4. *Zoom Out* by clicking the green arrow next to the ***Save*** button. Click ***Return Tank*** on the gas cylinder. On the table underneath the experimental chamber is a switch to choose Real gases or Ideal gases. Click on the ***Ideal Gases*** and choose the cylinder labeled *Ideal 8* (Ideal 8 MW = 222 g/mol). Click on the balloon chamber to *Zoom In* and set the temperature, pressure, and moles to 298 K, 1.00 atm, and 0.300 moles, respectively. Repeat the experiment with this gas labeling the data link as 'Ideal Gas 8.'

5. *Zoom Out* by clicking on the green arrow next to the ***Save*** button. Click on the *Stockroom* and then on the *Clipboard* and select *Balloon Experiment N2*. Again, set the temperature, pressure, and moles to 298 K, 1.00 atm, and 0.300 moles, respectively. You may have to click on the ***Units*** button to change some of the variables to the correct units. Repeat the experiment with this gas labeling the data link 'Real Gas N2.'

6. Select the lab book and click on the data link for Ideal Gas 1. In the *Data Viewer* window, select all the data by clicking on the ***Select All*** button and copy the data using CTRL-C for Windows or CMD-C for Macintosh. Paste the data into a spreadsheet program and create a graph with volume on the *x*-axis and pressure on the *y*-axis. Also create a graph for your data from Ideal Gas 8 and Real Gas N2.

7. *Based on your data, what relationship exists between the pressure and the volume of a gas (assuming a constant temperature)?* _____

_____

8. *Look up a statement of Boyle's Law in your textbook. Do your results further prove this?* _____

9. Complete the tables from the data saved in your lab book. Use only a sampling of the data for pressures at 1, 3, 6, and 9 atm.

Ideal Gas 1 MW = 4 g/mol

Volume (L)	Pressure (atm)	*PV* Product ($P \times V$)

Ideal Gas 8 MW = 222 g/mol

Volume (L)	Pressure (atm)	*PV* Product ($P \times V$)

Real Gas N2

Volume (L)	Pressure (atm)	*PV* Product ($P \times V$)

10. *What conclusions can you make about the PV product with Ideal Gas 1, MW = 4 g/mol?*

_____

How is the PV product affected using an ideal gas with a different molecular weight (Ideal Gas 8)?

_____

11. *How are your results affected using a Real Gas (N2)?* _____

_____

12. You may want to repeat the experiment several times using different size pressure changes.

VCL 6-2: Charles's Law: Temperature and Volume

Charles' Law was discovered by Joseph Louis Gay-Lussac in 1802; it was based on unpublished work done by Jacques Charles in about 1787. Charles had found that a number of gases expand to the same extent over the same 80 degree temperature interval. You will be observing the relationship between the temperature and volume of a gas similar to that studied by Charles.

1. Start *Virtual ChemLab* and select *Charles's Law: Temperature and Volume* from the list of assignments. The lab will open in the Gases laboratory.

2. Note that the balloon in the chamber is filled with 0.050 moles of an ideal gas (MW = 4 g/mol) at a temperature of 100°C, a pressure of 1.00 atm, and a volume of 1.531 L. To the left of the Temperature LCD controller is a lever that will decrease and increase the temperature as it is moved up or down; the digit changes depending on how far the lever is moved. Digits may also be clicked directly to type in the desired number, or they can be rounded by clicking on the ***R*** button. You may want to practice adjusting the lever so that you can decrease and increase the temperature accurately. Make sure the moles, temperature, and pressure are returned to their original values before proceeding.

3. Click on the *Lab Book* to open it. Back in the laboratory, click on the ***Save*** button to start recording *P, V, T,* and *n* data to the lab book. Increase the temperature from 100°C to 1000°C 100 degrees at a time. Click ***Stop*** to stop recording data, and a blue data link will appear in the lab book. To help keep track of your data links, enter 'Ideal Gas 1' next to the link.

4. *Zoom Out* by clicking on the green arrow next to the ***Save*** button. Click on the *Stockroom* and then on the *Clipboard* and select *Balloon Experiment N2*. Again, set the temperature, pressure, and moles to 100°C, 1.00 atm, and 0.050 moles, respectively. You may have to click on the ***Units*** button to change some of the variables to the correct units. Repeat the experiment with this gas labeling the data link 'Real Gas N2.'

5. Select the lab book and click on the data link for Ideal Gas 1. In the *Data Viewer* window, select all the data by clicking on the ***Select All*** button and copy the data using CTRL-C for Windows or CMD-C for Macintosh. Paste the data into a spreadsheet program and create a graph with temperature on the *x*-axis and volume on the *y*-axis. Also create a graph for the data labeled Real Gas N2.

6. *Based on your data, what relationship exists between the temperature and the volume of a gas (assuming a constant pressure)?* _____

   _____

7. *Look up a statement of Charles' Law in your textbook. Do your results further prove this?* _____

8. Using the spreadsheet program, fit the ideal gas data to a line or printout the graph and use a ruler to draw the best line through the data. The lowest possible temperature is reached when an ideal gas has zero volume. This temperature is the *x*-intercept for the plotted line.

   What is this temperature? _____

9. *Now do the same analysis with the real gas data (N2). What temperature did you find?* _____

10. *Under these conditions, does N_2 behave like an ideal gas?* _____

VCL 6-3: Avogadro's Law: Moles and Volume

In 1808, Joseph Gay-Lussac observed the *law of combining values,* which states that the volumes of gases that react with one another react in the ratio of small whole numbers. Three years later, Amedeo Avogadro built upon this observation by proposing what is now known as *Avogadro's hypothesis*: Equal volumes of gases at the same temperature and pressure contain equal numbers of molecules. Avogadro's Law, which states the relationship between moles and volume, followed from his hypothesis. You will be observing the same principle that Avogadro stated two hundred years ago.

1. Start *Virtual ChemLab* and select *Avogadro's Law: Moles and Volume* from the list of assignments. The lab will open in the Gases laboratory. You will see LCD controllers on the left for volume, pressure, temperature and number of moles. You may change the units for volume, pressure, and temperature by clicking on the ***Units*** buttons. The balloon has been filled with 0.100 moles of an ideal gas and the pressure is 2.00 atm. Record the number of moles and the volume (in L) in the data table below.

2. Click on the tenths digit on the Moles LCD controller and change the moles of gas in the balloon from 0.1 to 0.2 mole. Record the number of moles and volume in the data table. Repeat for 0.3, 0.4, and 0.5 moles.

Data Table

n (moles)	*V* (L)

3. *Based on your observations, what can you state about the relationship between moles and volume of a gas?* _____

_____

4. *Write a mathematical equation using a proportionality constant (k) with units of L/mol that expresses what you have learned about Avogadro's Law. Determine the value of k.*

VCL 6-4: Derivation of the Ideal Gas Law

An ideal gas is a hypothetical gas whose pressure, volume, and temperature follow the relationship $PV = nRT$. Ideal gases do not actually exist, although all real gases can behave like an ideal gas at certain temperatures and pressures. All gases can be described to some extent using the Ideal Gas Law, and it is important in our understanding of how all gases behave. In this assignment, you will derive the Ideal Gas Law from experimental observations.

The state of any gas can be described using the four variables: pressure (P), volume (V), temperature (T), and the number of moles of gas (n). Each experiment in *Virtual ChemLab: Gases* allows three of these variables (the independent variables) to be manipulated or changed and shows the effect on the remaining variable (the dependent variable).

1. Start *Virtual ChemLab* and select *Ideal Gas Law* from the list of assignments. The lab will open in the Gases laboratory.

2. Use the balloon experiment already setup in the laboratory to describe the relationship between pressure (P) and volume (V). Increase and decrease the pressure using the lever on the Pressure LCD controller to determine the effect on volume.

   What can you conclude about the effect of pressure on volume? Write a mathematical relationship using the proportionality symbol ($\propto$).

   _____

3. Use this same experiment to describe the relationship between temperature (T) and volume by increasing and decreasing the temperature.

   What can you conclude about the effect of temperature on volume? Write a mathematical relationship using the proportionality symbol ($\propto$).

   _____

4. Use this same experiment to describe the relationship between moles of gas and volume by increasing and decreasing the number of moles (n).

   What can you conclude about the effect of moles on volume? Write a mathematical relationship using the proportionality symbol ($\propto$).

   _____

5. Since volume is inversely proportional to pressure and directly proportional to temperature and moles, we can combine these three relationships into a single proportionality by showing how V is proportional to $1/P$, T, and n.

   Write one combined proportion to show the relationship of volume to pressure, temperature and moles.

---

6. This proportional relationship can be converted into a mathematical equation by inserting a proportionality constant (R) into the numerator on the right side.

   Write this mathematical equation and rearrange with P on the left side with V.

---

7. This equation is known as the Ideal Gas Law.

   Using data for volume, temperature, pressure and moles from one of the gas experiments, calculate the value for R with units of $L \cdot atm \cdot K^{-1} \cdot mol^{-1}$. *(Show all work and round to three significant digits).*

---

8. *Using the conversion between atmospheres and mm Hg (1 atm = 760 mm Hg), calculate the value for R with units of* $L \cdot mm\ Hg \cdot K^{-1} \cdot mol^{-1}$. *(Show all work and round to three significant digits).*

---

9. *Using the conversion between atmospheres and kPa (1 atm = 101.3 kPa), calculate the value for R with units of* $L \cdot kPa \cdot K^{-1} \cdot mol^{-1}$. *(Show all work and round to three significant digits).*

VCL 6-5: Dalton's Law of Partial Pressures

Dalton's Law of Partial Pressures, named after its discoverer John Dalton, describes the behavior of gas mixtures. It states that the total pressure of the gas, P_{tot}, is the sum of the partial pressures of each gas, or the sum of the pressures that each gas would exert if it were alone in the container. In this assignment you will become more familiar with Dalton's law.

1. Start *Virtual ChemLab* and select *Dalton's Law of Partial Pressures* from the list of assignments. The lab will open in the Gases laboratory. You will see a gas experiment with eight gas cylinders on the right. Make certain that the switch on the lower right of the lab bench is set to Ideal Gases. Note that the Ideal Gases each have a different molecular weight.

2. Select one of the Ideal Gas cylinders by clicking on the white label. Click the red arrow on the brass cylinder valve until the meter reads 400. Add this Ideal Gas to the balloon by clicking the green ***Open Valve*** switch once to add gas and again to stop. Add an amount of your choice but do not fill the balloon too full since you will be adding two additional gases. Click ***Return Tank***.

3. Repeat step # 2 for two additional Ideal Gases of your choice. Make certain that you do not explode the balloon. If you do, click the ***Reset*** button located on the upper right of the gas chamber and repeat the experiment.

4. Click on the experimental apparatus to *Zoom In*. There are four LCD controllers on the left for volume, pressure, temperature, and number of moles. You can change the units for volume, pressure and temperature by clicking on the ***Units*** button on each controller. Under pressure and number of moles are numbers 1-8 that correspond to Ideal Gases 1-8. The three gases that you selected will be highlighted. Clicking on each highlighted number will display the pressure or moles for that gas alone. Find the Ideal Gas number, the number of moles, and the partial pressure for each of your three Ideal Gases. Record this in the data table.

Data Table

Ideal Gas Number	Moles (n)	Partial Pressure (P_i)

5. *Using the information from the data table, determine the total pressure in the balloon.*

_____

6. Click ***Total*** on the Pressure controller. Compare your answer from # 5 to the total pressure on the meter.

   Write both pressures below and write a mathematical equation to represent what you have learned about Dalton's Law.

7. Another way of expressing Dalton's Law of Partial Pressures is with the expression $P_i = x_i P_{total}$ where P_i is the partial pressure of gas i, x_i is the mole fraction of that gas in the gas mixture, and P_{total} is the total pressure.

Verify that this relationship holds using the data you have collected and record you results in the data table below.

Data Table

Ideal Gas Number	x_i	P_i (Calculated)	P_i (Measured)

VCL 6-6: Ideal vs. Real Gases

At room temperature and normal atmospheric pressures, real gases behave similarly to ideal gases, but real gases can deviate significantly from ideal gas behavior at extreme conditions such as high temperatures and high pressures. It is not always easy to find an effective means to show the deviation from ideal gas behavior for real gases. An effective but simple method to see these deviations is to calculate the value of R, the ideal gas constant, for real gases *assuming* they follow the ideal gas law and then compare the value of R with the actual value of 0.08205 $L \cdot atm \cdot K^{-1} \cdot mol^{-1}$. In this assignment, you will measure P, V, T, and n for various real gases under different conditions and then you will calculate the value of R and compare it with its actual value.

1. Start *Virtual ChemLab* and select *Ideal vs. Real Gases* from the list of assignments. The lab will open in the Gases laboratory with the balloon filled with 0.100 moles of Ideal Gas 1.

2. Click on the ***Units*** buttons to change the units to L or mL for volume, atm for pressure, and K for temperature. On the left of the gas chamber are LCD controllers for the volume, pressure, temperature, and moles. On the left of the Pressure, Temperature, and Moles LCD controllers is a lever that will decrease and increase the pressure, temperature, or moles as the lever is moved up or down; the digit changes depending on how far the lever is moved. Digits may also be clicked directly to type in the desired number. Clicking to the left of the farthest left digit will add the next place; for example, if you have 1.7 atm you can click left of the 1 and enter 2 to make it 21.7 atm or click left of the 2 and enter 5 to make it 521.7 atm. The small ***R*** button in the upper left corner rounds the number. Clicking several times will round from ones to tens to hundreds.

   The green arrow to the left of the ***Save*** button will *Zoom Out*. Clicking ***Return Tank*** on the gas cylinder will return the tank to the rack and allow you to select a different gas. Clicking the gas chamber will *Zoom In* to allow you to change parameters. Be careful not to make the balloon so large that it bursts. If it does, click the red ***Reset*** button in the top right and then reset your units and values for each parameter. Remember that volume must be in L. If mL appears, you must convert to L in your calculations.

3. *Complete the data table for the following gases and conditions (all with 0.100 mole):*

   a. Ideal gas at low $T = 10$ K, high $T = 1000$ K, low $P = 1$ atm, high $P = 15$ atm
   b. Methane gas (CH_4) at low $T = 160$ K, high $T = 400$ K, low $P = 1$ atm, high $P = 15$ atm
   c. Carbon dioxide gas (CO_2) at low $T = 250$ K, high $T = 1000$ K, low $P = 1$ atm, high $P = 15$ atm

Data Table

Gas	V (L)	P (atm)	T (K)	n (mol)
Ideal, low T, low P				
Ideal, low T, high P				
Ideal, high T, low P				
Ideal, high T, high P				
CH_4, low T, low P				
CH_4, low T, high P				
CH_4, high T, low P				
CH_4, high T, high P				

CO_2, low *T*, low *P*				
CO_2, low *T*, high *P*				
CO_2, high *T*, low *P*				
CO_2, high *T*, high *P*				

4. If $PV = nRT$ then $R = PV/nT$.

   Complete the results table for each experiment above. Use four significant digits.

Results Table

Gas	Calculated *R* ($L \cdot atm \cdot K^{-1} \cdot mol^{-1}$)
Ideal, low *T*, low *P*	
Ideal, low *T*, high *P*	
Ideal, high *T*, low *P*	
Ideal, high *T*, high *P*	
CH_4, low *T*, low *P*	
CH_4, low *T*, high *P*	
CH_4, high *T*, low *P*	
CH_4, high *T*, high *P*	
CO_2, low *T*, low *P*	
CO_2, low *T*, high *P*	
CO_2, high *T*, low *P*	
CO_2, high *T*, high *P*	

5. *Which gases and conditions show significant deviation from the actual value of R? Explain.*

_____

_____

_____

_____

VCL 6-7: The Effect of Mass on Pressure

An understanding of pressure is an integral part of our understanding of the behavior of gases. Pressure is defined as the force per unit area exerted by a gas or other medium. The pressure of a gas is affected by many variables, such as temperature, external pressure, volume, moles of a gas, and other factors. This assignment will help you become more familiar with pressure and the effect of adding mass to a frictionless, massless piston.

1. Start *Virtual ChemLab* and select *The Effect of Mass on Pressure* from the list of assignments. The lab will open in the Gases laboratory.

2. This experiment consists of a cylinder with a frictionless-massless piston. When the experiment starts, the chamber is filled with the selected gas. Clicking on the ***Piston*** button moves the piston onto the cylinder and traps the gas in the cylinder. The moles of gas trapped in the cylinder and the volume of gas are measured using the Moles/Volume LCD controller. Pressure can be exerted on the gas in the cylinder by adjusting the external pressure in the chamber and by adding mass to the top of the piston (or $P_{int} = P_{mass} + P_{ext}$ where P_{int} is the internal pressure or the pressure of the gas in the cylinder, P_{mass} is the pressure being exerted on the gas by adding weights to the piston, and P_{ext} is the pressure being exerted on the piston by the gas in the chamber). If there is no mass on the piston, then $P_{int} = P_{ext}$.

3. Click the green ***Piston*** button to move the piston onto the cylinder. Record the mass (force, in tons) and the internal pressure (in psi) in the data table.

4. Click on the tenths place for mass and add 0.5 tons of mass to the piston. Record the mass and internal pressure in the Data Table. Repeat this for 2.5 tons (the weight of a small car).

Data Table

Mass (tons)	External Pressure (psi)	Calculated Internal Pressure (psi)	Measured Internal Pressure (psi)

5. You must now calculate the pressure being exerted by the 0.5 tons or, P_{mass}. First, convert tons to psi (pounds per square inch).

   How many pounds is 0.5 tons? _____

   The diameter of the piston is 15 cm. What is the radius (in cm)? _____

   1 inch = 2.54 cm.

   What is the radius of the piston in inches? _____

   The area of the circular piston is found by $A = \pi r^2$.

   What is the area of the piston in square inches (in^2)? _____

The pressure exerted on the piston by the added mass in pounds per square inch (psi) can be determined by dividing the mass in pounds by the area in square inches.

What is the pressure exerted by the added mass in psi? _____

The internal pressure is the sum of the external pressure and the added mass.

What is the calculated internal pressure? Compare your calculated answer with the internal pressure meter answer. How do they compare?

_____

6. *Predict the internal pressure (in psi) when 2.5 tons are added.* _____

How does your calculated answer compare with the internal pressure meter when you add 2.5 tons of mass? Record your data in the data table.

_____

VCL 7-1: Specific Heat of Pb

On a sunny day, the water in a swimming pool may warm up a degree or two while the concrete around the pool may become too hot to walk on with bare feet. This may seem strange since the water and concrete are being heated by the same source—the sun. This evidence suggests that it takes more heat to raise the temperature of some substances than others, which is true. The amount of heat required to raise the temperature of 1 g of a substance by 1 degree is called the *specific heat capacity* or *specific heat* of that substance. Water, for instance, has a specific heat of 4.18 J/K·g. This value is high in comparison with the specific heats for other materials, such as concrete or metals. In this experiment, you will use a simple calorimeter and your knowledge of the specific heat of water to measure the specific heat of lead (Pb).

1. Start *Virtual ChemLab* and select *The Specific Heat of Pb* from the list of assignments. The lab will open in the Calorimetry laboratory.

2. Click on the *Lab Book* to open it. Record the mass of Pb on the balance. If it is too small to read click on the *Balance* area to zoom in, record the mass of Pb in the data table below, and return to the laboratory.

3. Pick up the Pb sample from the balance pan and place the sample in the oven. Click the oven door to close. The oven is set to heat to 200°C.

4. The calorimeter has been filled with 100 mL water. The density of water at 25°C is 0.998 g/mL. Use the density of the water to determine the mass of water from the volume and record the volume and mass in the data table.

   Make certain the stirrer is ***On*** (you should be able to see the shaft rotating). Click the thermometer window to bring it to the front and click ***Save*** to begin recording data. Allow 20-30 seconds to obtain a baseline temperature of the water. You can observe the temperature in the calorimeter as a function of time using the graph window.

5. Click on the *Oven* to open it. Drag the hot Pb sample from the oven until it snaps into place above the calorimeter and drop it in. Click the thermometer and graph windows to bring them to the front again and observe the change in temperature in the graph window until it reaches a constant value and then wait an additional 20-30 seconds. Click ***Stop*** in the temperature window. (You can click on the clock on the wall labeled *Accelerate* to accelerate the time in the laboratory.) A blue data link will appear in the lab book. Click the blue data link and record the temperature before adding the Pb and the *highest* temperature after adding the Pb in the data table. (Remember that the water will begin to cool down after reaching the equilibrium temperature.)

Data Table

	Pb
mass of metal (g)	
volume of water (mL)	
mass of water (g)	
initial temperature of water (°C)	
initial temperature of metal (°C)	
max temp of water + metal (°C)	

6. *Calculate the changes in temperature of the water (ΔT_{water}).* _____

_____

7. *Calculate the heat (q), in J, gained by the water using the following equation:*

$$q_{\text{water}} = m_{\text{water}} \times \Delta T_{\text{water}} \times C_{\text{water}}, \text{ given } C_{\text{water}} = 4.184 \text{ J/(K·g)}$$

_____

8. *Calculate the changes in temperature of the Pb (ΔT_{Pb}).* _____

_____

9. *Remembering that the heat gained by the water is equal to the heat lost by the metal, calculate the specific heat of lead in J/K·g.*

$$q_{\text{water}} = -q_{\text{metal}} = m_{\text{Pb}} \times \Delta T_{\text{Pb}} \times C_{\text{Pb}} \text{ and } C_{\text{Pb}} = \frac{q_{\text{metal}}}{(m_{\text{metal}})(\Delta T_{\text{metal}})}$$

_____

10. *Calculate the percent error in the specific heat value that you determined experimentally.* The accepted value for Pb is 0.130 J/ K·g.

$$\%\ Error = \frac{|your\ answer - accepted\ answer|}{accepted\ answer} \times 100$$

$$\%\ Error =$$

VCL 7-2: Specific Heat of Al

On a sunny day, the water in a swimming pool may warm up a degree or two while the concrete around the pool may become too hot to walk on with bare feet. This may seem strange since the water and concrete are being heated by the same source—the sun. This evidence suggests that it takes more heat to raise the temperature of some substances than others, which is true. The amount of heat required to raise the temperature of 1 g of a substance by 1 degree is called the *specific heat capacity* or *specific heat* of that substance. Water, for instance, has a specific heat of 4.18 J/K·g. This value is high in comparison with the specific heats for other materials, such as concrete or metals. In this experiment, you will use a simple calorimeter and your knowledge of the specific heat of water to measure the specific heat of aluminum (Al).

1. Start *Virtual ChemLab* and select *The Specific Heat of Al* from the list of assignments. The lab will open in the Calorimetry laboratory.

2. Click on the *Lab Book* to open it. Record the mass of Al on the balance. If it is too small to read click on the *Balance* area to zoom in, record the mass of Al in the data table below, and return to the laboratory.

3. Pick up the Al sample from the balance pan and place the sample in the oven. Click the oven door to close. The oven is set to heat to 200°C.

4. The calorimeter has been filled with 100 mL water. The density of water at 25°C is 0.998 g/mL. Use the density of the water to determine the mass of water from the volume and record the volume and mass in the data table.

   Make certain the stirrer is ***On*** (you should be able to see the shaft rotating). Click the thermometer window to bring it to the front and click ***Save*** to begin recording data. Allow 20-30 seconds to obtain a baseline temperature of the water. You can observe the temperature in the calorimeter as a function of time using the graph window.

5. Click on the *Oven* to open it. Drag the hot Al sample from the oven until it snaps into place above the calorimeter and drop it in. Click the thermometer and graph windows to bring them to the front again and observe the change in temperature in the graph window until it reaches a constant value and then wait an additional 20-30 seconds. Click ***Stop*** in the temperature window. (You can click on the clock on the wall labeled *Accelerate* to accelerate the time in the laboratory.) A blue data link will appear in the lab book. Click the blue data link and record the temperature before adding the Al and the *highest* temperature after adding the Al in the data table. (Remember that the water will begin to cool down after reaching the equilibrium temperature.)

Data Table

	Al
mass of metal (g)	
volume of water (mL)	
mass of water (g)	
initial temperature of water (°C)	
initial temperature of metal (°C)	
max temp of water + metal (°C)	

6. *Calculate the change in temperature of the water* (ΔT_{water}). _____

_____

7. *Calculate the heat (q), in J, gained by the water using the following equation:*

$$q_{\text{water}} = m_{\text{water}} \times \Delta T_{\text{water}} \times C_{\text{water}}, \text{ given } C_{\text{water}} = 4.184 \text{ J/(K·g)}$$

_____

8. *Calculate the changes in temperature of the Al* (ΔT_{Al}). _____

_____

9. *Remembering that the heat gained by the water is equal to the heat lost by the metal, calculate the specific heat of aluminum in J/K·g.*

$$q_{\text{water}} = -q_{\text{metal}} = m_{\text{Al}} \times \Delta T_{\text{Al}} \times C_{\text{Al}} \text{ and } C_{\text{Al}} = \frac{q_{\text{metal}}}{(m_{\text{metal}})(\Delta T_{\text{metal}})}$$

_____

10. *Calculate the percent error in the specific heat value that you determined experimentally.* The accepted value for Al is 0.903 J/ K·g.

$$\%\ Error = \frac{|your\ answer - accepted\ answer|}{accepted\ answer} \times 100$$

$\%\ Error =$

VCL 7-3: Endothermic vs. Exothermic

In various chemical processes such as reactions and the dissolving of salts, heat is either absorbed or given off. We call these events either an endothermic (heat in) or exothermic (heat out) process. It is usual to detect these heat events by measuring the temperature change associated with the process. In this problem, you will dissolve several salts in water, measure the resulting temperature change, and then make deductions about the nature of the process.

1. Start *Virtual ChemLab* and select *Endothermic vs. Exothermic* from the list of assignments. The lab will open in the Calorimetry laboratory.

2. There will be a bottle of sodium chloride (NaCl) on the lab bench. A weigh paper will be on the balance with approximately 2 g of NaCl on the paper.

3. The calorimeter will be on the lab bench and filled with 100 mL water. Click the *Lab Book* to open it. Make certain the stirrer is ***On*** (you should be able to see the shaft rotating). In the thermometer window click ***Save*** to begin recording data. Allow 20-30 seconds to obtain a baseline temperature of the water.

4. Drag the weigh paper with the sample to the calorimeter until it snaps into place and then pour the sample into the calorimeter. Observe the change in temperature until it reaches a maximum and then record data for an additional 20-30 seconds. Click ***Stop***. (You can click on the clock on the wall labeled *Accelerate* to accelerate the time in the laboratory.) A blue data link will appear in the lab book. Click the data link and record the temperature before adding the NaCl and the *highest* or *lowest* temperature after adding the NaCl in the data table.

5. Click the red disposal bucket to clear the lab. Click on the Stockroom to enter. Click on the clipboard and select Preset Experiment #7 and repeat the experiment with $NaNO_3$. Record the initial and final temperatures in the data table.

6. Click the red disposal bucket to clear the lab. Click on the Stockroom to enter. Click the clipboard and select Preset Experiment #8 and repeat the experiment with $NaCH_3COO$ (NaAc). Record the initial and final temperatures in the data table.

Data Table

Mixture	T_1	T_2	ΔT (T_2-T_1)
NaCl (s) + H_2O (l)			
$NaNO_3$ (s) + H_2O (l)			
$NaCH_3COO$ + H_2O (l)			

Use your experimental data to answer the following questions.

7. *Calculate ΔT ($\Delta T = T_2 - T_1$) for each mixture and record it in the data table.*

8. An exothermic process gives off heat (warms up). An endothermic process absorbs heat (cools off). *Which solutions are endothermic and which are exothermic? What is the sign of the change in enthalpy (ΔH) in each case?* _____

_____

9. *Which solution(s) had little or no change in temperature?* _____

VCL 7-4: Heat of Combustion: Sugar

The heat of combustion (ΔH_{comb}) is the heat of reaction for the complete burning (reacting with O_2) of one mole of a substance to form CO_2 and H_2O. Calorimetry experiments that measure the heat of combustion can be performed at constant volume using a device called a bomb calorimeter. In a bomb calorimeter a sample is burned in a constant-volume chamber in the presence of oxygen at high pressure. The heat that is released warms the water surrounding the chamber. By measuring the temperature increase of the water, it is possible to calculate the quantity of heat released during the combustion reaction. In this assignment you will calculate the heat of combustion of sugar (sucrose, $C_{12}H_{22}O_{11}$). The calorimeter has already been calibrated by combusting benzoic acid.

1. Start *Virtual ChemLab* and select *Heat of Combustion: Sugar* from the list of assignments. The lab will open in the Calorimetry laboratory with the bomb calorimeter out and disassembled and with a sample of sugar in the calorimeter cup on the balance. The balance has already been tared.

2. Click on the *Lab Book* to open it.

3. Record the mass of the sugar sample from the balance. If you cannot read it click on the *Balance* area to zoom in, record the mass in the data table below and return to the laboratory.

4. Double-click the following (in numerical order) to assemble the calorimeter: (1) the cup on the balance pan, (2) the bomb head, (3) the screw cap, and (4) the bomb. Click the calorimeter lid to close it. Combustion experiments can take a considerable length of time. Click the clock on the wall labeled *Accelerate* to accelerate the laboratory time.

5. Click the bomb control panel and the plot window to bring them to the front. Click on the ***Save*** button to save data to the lab book. Allow the graph to proceed for 20-30 seconds to establish a baseline temperature.

6. Click ***Ignite*** and observe the graph. When the temperature has leveled off (up to 5 minutes of laboratory time), click ***Stop***. A blue data link will appear in the lab book. Click the blue data link to view the collected data. Record the temperature before and after ignition of the sugar sample in the data table.

Data Table

	sucrose ($C_{12}H_{22}O_{11}$)
mass of sample (g)	
initial temperature (°C)	
final temperature (°C)	

7. *Write a complete balanced chemical equation for the combustion of sucrose.* _____

_____

8. *Calculate ΔT for the water using $\Delta T = |T_f - T_i|$.* _____

9. *Calculate the moles of sucrose in the sample ($MW_{sucrose}$ = 342.3 g/mol).*

10. ΔH_{comb} for sucrose can be calculated using $\Delta H_{comb} = (C_{system}\Delta T)/n$, where n is the moles of sucrose in the sample and C_{system} is the heat capacity of the calorimetric system.

    Use 10.310 kJ/K for C_{system} and calculate the heat of combustion, in kJ/mol, for sucrose.

11. *If the accepted value for the heat of combustion for sugar is 5639 kJ/mol calculate the percent error.*

$$\%\ Error = \frac{|your\ answer - accepted\ answer|}{accepted\ answer} \times 100$$

$$\%\ Error =$$

This experiment does not consider that all of the conditions are standard state conditions; therefore, you are calculating ΔH_{comb} **not** ΔH^{o}_{comb}.

VCL 7-5: Heat of Combustion: Chicken Fat

The heat of combustion (ΔH_{comb}) is the heat of reaction for the complete burning (reacting with O_2) of one mole of a substance to form CO_2 and H_2O. Calorimetry experiments that measure the heat of combustion can be performed at constant volume using a device called a bomb calorimeter. In a bomb calorimeter a sample is burned in a constant-volume chamber in the presence of oxygen at high pressure. The heat that is released warms the water surrounding the chamber. By measuring the temperature increase of the water, it is possible to calculate the quantity of heat released during the combustion reaction. In this assignment you will calculate the heat of combustion of chicken fat. The calorimeter has already been calibrated by combusting benzoic acid.

1. Start *Virtual ChemLab* and select *Heat of Combustion: Chicken Fat* from the list of assignments. The lab will open in the Calorimetry laboratory with the bomb calorimeter out and disassembled and with a sample of chicken fat in the calorimeter cup on the balance. The balance has already been tared.

2. Click on the *Lab Book* to open it.

3. Record the mass of the chicken fat sample from the balance. If you cannot read it click on the *Balance* area to zoom in, record the mass in the data table below and return to the laboratory.

4. Double-click the following (in numerical order) to assemble the calorimeter: (1) the cup on the balance pan, (2) the bomb head, (3) the screw cap, and (4) the bomb. Click the calorimeter lid to close it. Combustion experiments can take a considerable length of time. Click the clock on the wall labeled *Accelerate* to accelerate the laboratory time.

5. Click the bomb control panel and the plot window to bring them to the front. Click on the ***Save*** button to save data to the lab book. Allow the graph to proceed for 20-30 seconds to establish a baseline temperature.

6. Click ***Ignite*** and observe the graph. When the temperature has leveled off (up to 5 minutes of laboratory time), click ***Stop***. A blue data link will appear in the lab book. Click the blue data link to view the collected data. Record the temperature before and after ignition of the chicken fat sample in the data table.

Data Table

	chicken fat
mass of sample (g)	
initial temperature (°C)	
final temperature (°C)	

7. *Calculate ΔT for the water using $\Delta T = |T_f - T_i|$.* _____

8. *Calculate the moles of chicken fat in the sample (MW_{fat} = 797.7 g/mol).*

9. ΔH_{comb} for chicken fat can be calculated using $\Delta H_{comb} = (C_{system}\Delta T)/n$, where n is the moles of chicken fat in the sample and C_{system} is the heat capacity of the calorimetric system.

   Use 10.310 kJ/K for C_{system} and calculate the heat of combustion, in kJ/mol, for chicken fat.

10. *If the accepted value for the heat of combustion for chicken fat is 30,038 kJ/mol calculate the percent error.*

$$\%\ Error = \frac{|your\ answer - accepted\ answer|}{accepted\ answer} \times 100$$

$$\%\ Error =$$

This experiment does not consider that all of the conditions are standard state conditions; therefore, you are calculating ΔH_{comb} **not** ΔH^{o}_{comb}.

11. The "calorie" used to measure the caloric content of foods is actually a kilocalorie (kcal) or 4184 kJ. *If the heat of combustion for sugar is 5639 kJ/mol, why are people who are on limited calorie diets advised to limit their fat intake?* _____

_____

_____

12. The food that we ingest is certainly not "combusted" in the same manner as is done in a bomb calorimeter.

    Why can we compare the heats of combustion of sugar or chicken fat measured in a bomb calorimeter with the caloric content of those foods? _____

_____

_____

_____

VCL 7-6: Heat of Combustion: TNT

The heat of combustion (ΔH_{comb}) is the heat of reaction for the complete burning (reacting with O_2) of one mole of a substance to form CO_2 and H_2O. Calorimetry experiments that measure the heat of combustion can be performed at constant volume using a device called a bomb calorimeter. In a bomb calorimeter a sample is burned in a constant-volume chamber in the presence of oxygen at high pressure. The heat that is released warms the water surrounding the chamber. By measuring the temperature increase of the water, it is possible to calculate the quantity of heat released during the combustion reaction. In this assignment you will calculate the heat of combustion of 2,4,6-trinitrotolune (TNT). The calorimeter has already been calibrated by combusting benzoic acid.

1. Start *Virtual ChemLab* and select *Heat of Combustion: TNT* from the list of assignments. The lab will open in the Calorimetry laboratory with the bomb calorimeter out and disassembled and with a sample of TNT in the calorimeter cup on the balance. The balance has already been tared.

2. Click on the *Lab Book* to open it.

3. Record the mass of the TNT sample from the balance. If you cannot read it click on the *Balance* area to zoom in, record the mass in the data table below and return to the laboratory.

4. Double-click the following (in numerical order) to assemble the calorimeter: (1) the cup on the balance pan, (2) the bomb head, (3) the screw cap, and (4) the bomb. Click the calorimeter lid to close it. Combustion experiments can take a considerable length of time. Click the clock on the wall labeled *Accelerate* to accelerate the laboratory time.

5. Click the bomb control panel and the plot window to bring them to the front. Click on the ***Save*** button to save data to the lab book. Allow the graph to proceed for 20-30 seconds to establish a baseline temperature.

6. Click ***Ignite*** and observe the graph. When the temperature has leveled off (up to 5 minutes of laboratory time), click ***Stop***. A blue data link will appear in the lab book. Click the blue data link to view the collected data. Record the temperature before and after ignition of the TNT sample in the data table.

Data Table

	2,4,6-trinitrotoluene (TNT)
mass of sample (g)	
initial temperature (°C)	
final temperature (°C)	

7. *Calculate ΔT for the water using $\Delta T = |T_f - T_i|$.* _____

8. *Calculate the moles of TNT in the sample (MW_{TNT} = 227.13 g/mol).*

9. ΔH_{comb} for TNT can be calculated using $\Delta H_{comb} = (C_{system}\Delta T)/n$, where n is the moles of TNT in the sample and C_{system} is the heat capacity, in kJ/mol, of the calorimetric system.

   Use 10.310 kJ/K for C_{system} and calculate the heat of combustion for TNT.

10. *If the accepted value for the heat of combustion for TNT is 3406 kJ/mol, calculate the percent error.*

$$\% \, Error = \frac{|your\ answer - accepted\ answer|}{accepted\ answer} \times 100$$

$$\% \, Error =$$

This experiment does not consider that all of the conditions are standard state conditions; therefore, you are calculating ΔH_{comb} **not** ΔH^{o}_{comb}.

11. *The heat of combustion for sugar is 5639 kJ/mole, but that for TNT is 3406 kJ/mole. Why, if the heat of combustion for TNT is smaller than for sugar, is TNT an explosive?* _____

_____

_____

VCL 7-7: Heat of Reaction: NaOH(aq) + HCl(aq)

Energy is either absorbed or released for all chemical reactions, and we call this energy the enthalpy of reaction (ΔH_{rxn}). If the enthalpy of reaction is positive, then we say that the energy was absorbed or that the reaction was *endothermic*. If the enthalpy of reaction is negative, then we say that energy was released or that the reaction was *exothermic*. Most chemical reactions are exothermic. In this problem, you will measure the amount of heat released when aqueous solutions of NaOH and HCl are mixed and react to form water and then you will calculate the heat of reaction.

$$NaOH(aq) + HCl(aq) = H_2O(l) + NaCl(aq)$$

1. Start *Virtual ChemLab* and select *Heat of Reaction: NaOH + HCl* from the list of assignments. The lab will open in the Calorimetry laboratory.

2. Click the *Lab Book* to open it. In the thermometer window click ***Save*** to begin recording data. Allow 20-30 seconds to obtain a baseline temperature of the water. Pour the first beaker containing 100 mL of 1.000 M HCl into the calorimeter and then pour the second beaker containing 100 mL of 1.000 M NaOH into the calorimeter. Observe the change in temperature until it reaches a maximum and then record data for an additional 20-30 seconds. Click ***Stop*** in the temperature window. (You can click on the clock on the wall labeled *Accelerate* to accelerate the time in the laboratory.) A blue data link will appear in the lab book. Click the blue data link and record the temperature before adding the NaOH and the *highest* temperature after adding the NaOH in the data table. (Remember that the water will begin to cool down after reaching the equilibrium temperature.)

Data Table

	NaOH/HCl
initial temperature (°C)	
final temperature (°C)	

3. *Is the observed reaction endothermic or exothermic? What will be the sign of ΔH_{rxn}?* _____

_____

4. *Calculate the change in temperature, ΔT.* Record your results in the results table on the following page.

5. *Calculate the mass of the reaction mixture in the calorimeter.* (To do this, first determine the total volume of the solution based on the assumption that the volumes are additive and that the density of the solution is the same as that of pure water, 1.0 g/mL.) Record your results in the results table.

_____

6. *Calculate the total heat released in the reaction, assuming that the specific heat capacity of the solution is the same as that of pure water, 4.184 J/K·g.* Record the result in the results table. Remember: heat of reaction = $m \times C \times \Delta T$

7. *Calculate the number of moles of NaOH used in the reaction by multiplying the volume of NaOH times the molarity (1.000 mol/L).* Record the results in the results table.

8. *Calculate ΔH_{rxn}, in kJ/mol, of NaOH for the reaction and record the results in the results table.* Make sure the sign of ΔH_{rxn} is correct.

Results Table

Mass of Rxn Mixture	ΔT	Total Heat Released	mol NaOH	ΔH_{rxn}/mol

VCL 7-8: Heat of Reaction: MgO(s) + HCl(aq)

Energy is either absorbed or released for all chemical reactions, and we call this energy the enthalpy of reaction (ΔH_{rxn}). If the enthalpy of reaction is positive, then we say that the energy was absorbed or that the reaction was *endothermic*. If the enthalpy of reaction is negative, then we say that energy was released or that the reaction was *exothermic*. Most chemical reactions are exothermic. In this problem, you will measure the amount of heat released when solid MgO is reacted with aqueous HCl to form water and then you will calculate the heat of reaction.

$$MgO(s) + 2HCl(aq) = H_2O(l) + MgCl_2(aq)$$

1. Start *Virtual ChemLab* and select *Heat of Reaction: MgO + HCl* from the list of assignments. The lab will open in the Calorimetry laboratory.

2. There will be a bottle of MgO near the balance. A weigh paper will be on the balance with approximately 2.81 g MgO on the paper. Record the mass of MgO in the data table.

3. The calorimeter will be on the lab bench and filled with 100 mL 1.000 M HCl. Make certain the stirrer is ***On*** (you should be able to see the shaft rotating). Click the *Lab Book* to open it. In the thermometer window click ***Save*** to begin recording data. Allow 20-30 seconds to obtain a baseline temperature of the HCl solution. Drag the weigh paper containing the MgO sample over to the calorimeter and drop the sample in. Observe the change in temperature until it reaches a maximum and then record data for an additional 20-30 seconds. Click ***Stop*** in the temperature window. (You can click on the clock on the wall labeled *Accelerate* to accelerate the time in the laboratory.) A blue data link will appear in the lab book. Click the blue data link and record the temperature before adding the MgO and the *highest* temperature after adding the MgO in the data table. (Remember that the water will begin to cool down after reaching the equilibrium temperature.)

Data Table

	NaOH/HCl
Mass MgO	
initial temperature (°C)	
final temperature (°C)	

4. *Is the observed reaction endothermic or exothermic? What will be the sign of ΔH_{rxn}?* _____

_____

5. *Calculate the change in temperature, ΔT. Record your results in the results table on the following page.*

6. *Calculate the mass of the reaction mixture in the calorimeter.* (To do this, assume that the density of the HCl solution originally in the calorimeter can be approximated with the density of water (1.0 g/mL). Record your results in the results table.

_____

7. *Calculate the total heat released in the reaction, in J, assuming that the specific heat capacity of the solution is the same as that of pure water, 4.184 J/K·g.* Record the result in the results table. Remember: heat of reaction = $m \times C \times \Delta T$

8. *Calculate the number of moles of MgO used in the reaction.* The molar mass of MgO is 56.305 g/mole. Record the results in the results table.

9. *Calculate ΔH_{rxn}, in kJ/mol, of MgO for the reaction and record the results in the results table.* Make sure the sign of ΔH_{rxn} is correct.

Results Table

Mass of Rxn Mixture	ΔT	Total Heat Released	mol MgO	ΔH_{rxn}/mol

VCL 7-9: Hess's Law

In this experiment, you will measure the amount of heat released in these three related exothermic reactions:

1. $NaOH\ (s) = Na^+\ (aq) + OH^-\ (aq) + \Delta H_1$
2. $NaOH\ (s) + H^+\ (aq) + Cl^-\ (aq) = H_2O + Na^+\ (aq) + Cl^-\ (aq) + \Delta H_2$
3. $Na^+\ (aq) + OH^-\ (aq) + H^+\ (aq) + Cl^-\ (aq) = H_2O + Na^+\ (aq) + Cl^-\ (aq) + \Delta H_3$

After determining the heats of reaction (ΔH_1, ΔH_2 and ΔH_3), you will then analyze your data and verify Hess's Law or $\Delta H_1 + \Delta H_3 = \Delta H_2$.

1. Start *Virtual ChemLab* and select *Hess's Law* from the list of assignments. The lab will open in the Calorimetry laboratory.

Reaction 1

2. There will be a bottle of NaOH near the balance. A weigh paper will be on the balance with approximately 4 g NaOH on the paper. Record the mass of NaOH in the data table on the following page.

3. The calorimeter will be on the lab bench and filled with 200 mL water. Click the *Lab Book* to open it. Make certain the stirrer is ***On*** (you should be able to see the shaft rotating). In the thermometer window click ***Save*** to begin recording data. Allow 20-30 seconds to obtain a baseline temperature of the water.

4. Drag the weigh paper with the sample to the calorimeter until it snaps into place and then pour the sample into the calorimeter. Observe the change in temperature until it reaches a maximum and then record data for an additional 20-30 seconds. Click ***Stop***. (You can click on the clock on the wall labeled *Accelerate* to accelerate the time in the laboratory.) A blue data link will appear in the lab book. Click the data link and record the initial and final water temperatures in the data table. If you need to repeat this part of the experiment, enter the Stockroom and select Preset Experiment #6 on the clipboard.

Reaction 2

5. Click the red disposal bucket to clear the lab. Click on the Stockroom to enter. Click on the clipboard and select Preset Experiment #5. Return to the laboratory.

6. There will be a bottle of NaOH near the balance. A weigh paper will be on the balance with approximately 4 g NaOH on the paper. Record the mass of NaOH in the data table. The calorimeter will be on the lab bench filled with 100 mL water, and there will be a beaker containing 100 mL of 1.000 M HCl on the lab bench. In the thermometer window click ***Save*** to begin recording data. Allow 20-30 seconds to obtain a baseline temperature of the water.

7. Make sure the beaker of HCl is visible and drag it to the calorimeter and pour it into the calorimeter. The HCl and the water are at the same temperature so there should be no temperature change. Now drag the weigh paper with the NaOH to the calorimeter until it snaps into place and pour the sample into the calorimeter. It is important that the HCl be added first and the NaOH added second. Observe

the change in temperature until it reaches a maximum and then record data for an additional 20-30 seconds. Record the temperature before adding the HCl and the temperature after adding the NaOH in the data table.

Reaction 3

8. Click the red disposal bucket to clear the lab. Click on the Stockroom to enter. Click on the clipboard and select Preset Experiment #4. Return to the laboratory.

9. In the thermometer window click ***Save*** to begin recording data. Allow 20-30 seconds to obtain a baseline temperature of the water. Pour the first beaker containing the HCl into the calorimeter and then pour the second beaker containing the NaOH into the calorimeter. Observe the change in temperature until it reaches a maximum and then record data for an additional 20-30 seconds. Record the initial and final temperatures in the data table.

Data Table

Parameter	Reaction 1	Reaction 2	Reaction 3
Mass NaOH			
initial temperature (°C)			
final temperature (°C)			

10. *Determine the change in temperature, ΔT, for each reaction.* Record your results in the results table on the following page.

11. *Calculate the mass of the reaction mixture in each reaction.* (To do this, first determine the total volume of the solution. Then calculate the mass of the solution, based on the assumption that the added solid does not change the volume and that the density of the solution is the same as that of pure water, 1.0 g/mL.) Remember to add the mass of the solid. Record your results in the result table.

12. *Calculate the total heat released in each reaction, in J, assuming that the specific heat capacity of the solution is the same as that of pure water, 4.184 J/K·g.* Record the result in the results table. Remember: heat of reaction = $m \times C \times \Delta T$

13. *Calculate the number of moles of NaOH used in reactions 1 and 2 where n = m/MW.* Record the results in the results table.

14. *Calculate the number of moles of NaOH used in reaction 3 by multiplying the volume of NaOH times the molarity (1.000 mol/L).* Record the results in the results table.

15. *Calculate the energy released, in kJ/mol, of NaOH for each reaction and record the results in the results table.*

Reaction 1

Reaction 2

Reaction 3

Results Table

Rxn #	Mass of Rxn Mixture	ΔT	Total Heat Released	mol NaOH	Heat Released per mol NaOH
1					
2					
3					

16. *Show that the equations for reactions 1 and 3, which are given in the background section, add up to equal the equation for reaction 2. Include the energy released per mole of NaOH in each equation.*

17. *Calculate the percent difference between the heat given off in reaction 2 and the sum of the heats given off in reactions 1 and 3. Assume that the heat given off in reaction 2 is correct.*

$$\%\ Difference = \frac{|heat_2 - (heat_1 + heat_3)|}{heat_2} \times 100$$

$\%\ Difference =$

18. *State in your own words what is meant by the additive nature of heats of reaction.* _____

_____

_____

_____

VCL 7-10: Heat of Formation: Aspirin

The heat of formation is the heat of reaction for the formation of a compound from its elements. The heat of formation can be determined by measuring the heat of combustion for the compound and then using Hess's law to convert the heat of combustion to a heat of formation. Calorimetry experiments that measure the heat of combustion can be performed at constant volume using a device called a bomb calorimeter. In a bomb calorimeter a sample is burned in a constant-volume chamber in the presence of oxygen at high pressure. The heat that is released warms the water surrounding the chamber. By measuring the temperature increase of the water, it is possible to calculate the quantity of heat released during the combustion reaction. In this assignment you will first measure the heat of combustion of aspirin ($C_9H_8O_4$) and then convert the heat of combustion to a heat of formation.

1. Start *Virtual ChemLab* and select *Heat of Formation: Aspirin* from the list of assignments. The lab will open in the Calorimetry laboratory with the bomb calorimeter out and disassembled and with a sample of asprin in the calorimeter cup on the balance. The balance has already been tared.

2. Click on the *Lab Book* to open it.

3. Record the mass of the aspirin sample from the balance. If you cannot read it click on the *Balance* area to zoom in, record the mass in the data table below and return to the laboratory.

4. Double-click the following (in numerical order) to assemble the calorimeter: (1) the cup on the balance pan, (2) the bomb head, (3) the screw cap, and (4) the bomb. Click the calorimeter lid to close it. Combustion experiments can take a considerable length of time. Click the clock on the wall labeled *Accelerate* to accelerate the laboratory time.

5. Click the bomb control panel and the plot window to bring them to the front. Click on the ***Save*** button to save data to the lab book. Allow the graph to proceed for 20-30 seconds to establish a baseline temperature.

6. Click ***Ignite*** and observe the graph. When the temperature has leveled off (up to 5 minutes of laboratory time), click ***Stop***. A blue data link will appear in the lab book. Click the blue data link to view the collected data. Record the temperature before and after ignition of the aspirin sample in the data table.

Data Table

	aspirin ($C_9H_8O_4$)
mass of sample (g)	
initial temperature (°C)	
final temperature (°C)	

7. *Write a complete balanced chemical equation for the combustion of aspirin.* _____

_____

8. *Calculate ΔT for the water using $\Delta T = |T_f - T_i|$.* _____

9. *Calculate the moles of aspirin in the sample ($MW_{aspirin}$ = 180.00 g/mol).*

10. ΔH_{comb} for aspirin can be calculated using $\Delta H_{comb} = (C_{system}\Delta T)/n$, where n is the moles of aspirin in the sample and C_{system} is the heat capacity of the calorimetric system.

    Use 10.310 kJ/K for C_{system} and calculate the heat of combustion, in kJ/mol, for aspirin. The heat of combustion will be negative since it is an exothermic reaction.

11. *Write an equation for the combustion of aspirin in the form $\Delta H_{comb} = \Sigma n\Delta H_f$ (products) – $\Sigma m\Delta H_f$ (reactants).*

12. *Calculate the heat of formation for aspirin given the standard enthalpies of formation for CO_2, H_2O, and O_2 are -393.5 kJ/mol, -285.83 kJ/mol, and 0 kJ/mol, respectively.*

This experiment does not consider that all of the conditions are standard state conditions; therefore, you are calculating ΔH_f **not** ΔH°_f.

VCL 7-11: Heat of Formation: Ethanol

The heat of formation is the heat of reaction for the formation of a compound from its elements. The heat of formation can be determined by measuring the heat of combustion for the compound and then using Hess's law to convert the heat of combustion to a heat of formation. Calorimetry experiments that measure the heat of combustion can be performed at constant volume using a device called a bomb calorimeter. In a bomb calorimeter a sample is burned in a constant-volume chamber in the presence of oxygen at high pressure. The heat that is released warms the water surrounding the chamber. By measuring the temperature increase of the water, it is possible to calculate the quantity of heat released during the combustion reaction. In this assignment you will first measure the heat of combustion of ethanol (ethyl alcohol, C_2H_5OH) and then convert the heat of combustion to a heat of formation.

1. Start *Virtual ChemLab* and select *Heat of Formation: Ethanol* from the list of assignments. The lab will open in the Calorimetry laboratory with the bomb calorimeter out and disassembled and with a sample of ethanol in the calorimeter cup on the balance. The balance has already been tared.

2. Click on the *Lab Book* to open it.

3. Record the mass of the ethanol sample from the balance. If you cannot read it click on the *Balance* area to zoom in, record the mass in the data table below and return to the laboratory.

4. Double-click the following (in numerical order) to assemble the calorimeter: (1) the cup on the balance pan, (2) the bomb head, (3) the screw cap, and (4) the bomb. Click the calorimeter lid to close it. Combustion experiments can take a considerable length of time. Click the clock on the wall labeled *Accelerate* to accelerate the laboratory time.

5. Click the bomb control panel and the plot window to bring them to the front. Click on the ***Save*** button to save data to the lab book. Allow the graph to proceed for 20-30 seconds to establish a baseline temperature.

6. Click ***Ignite*** and observe the graph. When the temperature has leveled off (up to 5 minutes of laboratory time), click ***Stop***. A blue data link will appear in the lab book. Click the blue data link to view the collected data. Record the temperature before and after ignition of the ethanol sample in the data table.

Data Table

	ethanol (C_2H_5OH)
mass of sample (g)	
initial temperature (°C)	
final temperature (°C)	

7. *Write a complete balanced chemical equation for the combustion of ethanol.*

_____

8. *Calculate ΔT for the water using $\Delta T = |T_f - T_i|$.* _____

9. *Calculate the moles of ethanol in the sample ($MW_{enthanol}$ = 46.00 g/mol).*

10. ΔH_{comb} for ethanol can be calculated using $\Delta H_{comb} = (C_{system}\Delta T)/n$, where n is the moles of ethanol in the sample and C_{system} is the heat capacity of the calorimetric system.

    Use 10.310 kJ/K for C_{system} and calculate the heat of combustion, in kJ/mol, for ethanol. The heat of combustion will be negative since it is an exothermic reaction.

11. *Write an equation for the combustion of ethanol in the form $\Delta H_{comb} = \Sigma n\Delta H_f$ (products) – $\Sigma m\Delta H_f$ (reactants).* _____

12. *Calculate the heat of formation for C_2H_5OH, given the standard enthalpies of formation for CO_2, H_2O, and O_2 are -393.5 kJ/mol, -285.83 kJ/mol, and 0 kJ/mol, respectively.*

13. *If the accepted value for the enthalpy of formation for ethanol is –277.7 kJ/mol, calculate the percent error.*

$$\%\ Error = \frac{|\text{your answer - accepted answer}|}{\text{accepted answer}} \times 100$$

$$\%\ Error =$$

This experiment does not consider that all of the conditions are standard state conditions; therefore, you are calculating ΔH_f **not** ΔH°_f.

VCL 8-1: Flame Tests for Metals

Have you ever wondered why a candle flame is yellow? The characteristic yellow of the flame comes from the glow of burning carbon fragments. The carbon fragments are produced by the incomplete combustion reaction of the wick and the candle wax. When elements, such as carbon, are heated to high temperatures, some of their electrons are excited to higher energy levels. When these excited electrons fall back to lower energy levels, they release excess energy in packages of light called photons. The color of the emitted light depends on the individual energy level spacing in the atom. When heated, each element emits a characteristic pattern of photons, which is useful for identifying the element. The characteristic colors of light produced when substances are heated in the flame of a gas burner are the basis for flame tests of several elements. In this assignment, you will perform flame tests that are used to identify several metallic elements.

1. Start *Virtual ChemLab* and select *Flame Tests for Metals* from the list of assignments. The lab will open in the Inorganic laboratory.

2. Enter the stockroom by clicking inside the *Stockroom* window. Once inside the stockroom, drag a test tube from the box and place it on the metal test tube stand. Bottles containing solutions of metal cations are located on the shelves, and you can click on any of the bottles to add them to your test tube. Click on the Na^+ bottle and click ***Done*** to send the test tube back to the lab. Repeat this process for each new metal cation until you have created test tubes containing Na^+, K^+, Ca^{2+}, Ba^{2+}, Sr^{2+}, and Cu^{2+}.

3. On the right side of the stockroom is a shelf labeled *Unknowns*. Click on the *Unknowns* label to create a test tube with an unknown. Now click on each of the following bottles on the shelf: Na^+, K^+, Ca^{2+}, Ba^{2+}, Sr^{2+}, and Cu^{2+}. Do not change the maximum and minimum on the left side and click on the green *Save* arrow. An unknown test tube labeled *Practice* will show up in the blue unknown rack on the unknown shelf. Drag the practice unknown test tube from the blue rack and place it in the metal stand and click on the *Return to Lab* arrow.

4. When you return to the lab you should note that you have seven test tubes. You will use the two flame test buttons at the bottom of the screen to perform a regular flame test and a flame test with a cobalt filter (blue glass held in front of the flame.) A test tube must be moved from the blue test tube rack to the metal test tube stand in order to perform the flame test. Test tubes dragged from the test tube rack can also be dropped on a test tube in the stand to switch places. Just above the periodic table there is a handle that, when clicked, pulls down the TV monitor. With the monitor down you can mouse-over each test tube to identify what metal cation is present in the test tube. As you mouse over each test tube, you will also see a picture of the test tube in the lower left corner.

5. Select the test tube containing Na^+ and place it on the metal stand. Click the ***Flame*** button. Record your observations in the data table on the following page. Click the ***Flame w/Cobalt*** button and record your observations in the same table.

6. Drag the K^+ test tube to the metal stand to exchange it with the Na^+. Perform a flame test on K^+ with and without cobalt glass. Record your observations in the data table.

7. For the other four ions, perform a regular flame test only. Do not use the cobalt glass. Record your observations in the data table.

Data Table

Flame Tests	[Answers]
Ion	Flame Color
sodium, Na^+	
sodium, Na^+ (cobalt glass)	
potassium, K^+	
potassium, K^+ (cobalt glass)	
calcium, Ca^{2+}	
barium, Ba^{2+}	
strontium, Sr^{2+}	
copper, Cu^{2+}	
unknown #1	
unknown #2	
unknown #3	
unknown #4	

8. Now perform a flame test on the practice unknown. Determine which of the six metal ions it most closely matches. You may repeat the flame test on any of the six metal ions if necessary. When you are confident that you have identified the unknown, open the *Lab Book* by clicking on it. On the left page, click the ***Report*** button. On the right page, click on the metal cation that you think is in the practice unknown. Click ***Submit*** and then ***OK***. If all of the cation buttons turn green, you have successfully identified the unknown. If any turn red then you are incorrect. Click on the red disposal bucket to clear all of your samples.

9. Return to the *Stockroom* and drag the practice unknown to the metal test tube stand. This will randomly create a new unknown. Click on the green *Return to lab* arrow and test and report this unknown. Continue until you have correctly identified four different practice unknowns.

10. The energy of colored light increases in the order red, yellow, green, blue, and violet.

    List the metallic elements used in the flame tests in increasing order of the energy of the light emitted.

11. *What is the purpose of using the cobalt glass in the identification of sodium and potassium?*

    _____

    _____

VCL 8-2: Atomic Emission Spectra

When a sample of gas is excited by applying a large alternating electric field, the gas emits light at certain discrete wavelengths. The intensity and wavelength of the light that is emitted is called the atomic emission spectrum and is unique for each gas. In this assignment, you will measure the emission spectra for several gases and then make some observations about the differences in their spectra.

1. Start *Virtual ChemLab* and select *Atomic Emission Spectra* from the list of assignments. The lab will open in the Quantum laboratory. The *Spectrometer* will be on the right of the lab table. The hydrogen emission spectra will be in the detector window in the upper right corner as a graph of Intensity vs. wavelength (λ).

2. *How many distinct lines do you see and what are their colors?* _____

_____

3. Click on the ***Visible/Full*** switch to magnify only the visible spectrum. You will see four peaks in the spectrum. If you drag your cursor over a peak, it will identify the wavelength (in nm) in the *x*-coordinate field in the bottom right corner of the detector window. Record the wavelengths of the four peaks in the visible hydrogen spectrum in the data table. (Round to whole numbers.)

4. The wavelength of each line can also be described in terms of its frequency. Use the wavelength of each line to calculate its frequency given that $\nu = c/\lambda$ where $c = 2.998 \times 10^{17}$ nm·s^{-1} (2.998×10^{8} m·s^{-1}). The energy (E) of a single quantum of light emitted by an atom is related to its frequency (ν) by the equation $E = h\nu$ where $h = 6.626 \times 10^{-34}$ J·s. Calculate the frequency of each line and the corresponding energy and record your results in the data Table.

Data Table

	λ (nm)	ν (1/s)	Energy (J)
Line #1 (left)			
Line #2			
Line #3			
Line #4 (right)			

5. Now, investigate the emission spectra for a different element, helium. Helium is the next element after hydrogen on the periodic table and has two electrons.

   Do you think the emission spectra for an atom with two electrons instead of one will be much different than hydrogen? _____

6. To exchange gas samples, double-click or click and drag the *Electric Field* and place it on the stockroom counter, and double-click or click and drag the *Gas (H_2)* sample tube and place it on the stockroom counter as well. You may have to first click on the main laboratory window in order to move the items.

7. Enter the stockroom by clicking in the *Stockroom*. Click on the *Gases* samples on the top shelf. Click on the cylinder labeled *He* to replace the H_2 in the sample tube with helium gas. If you point to the gas sample tube with the cursor it should read *He*.

8. Return to the laboratory and drag the gas sample tube off the stockroom counter and place it in the middle of the table as indicated by the spotlight. Drag the *Electric Field* and place it on the gas sample tube. Carefully click the button just above the left zero on the *Electric Field* controller and change the voltage to 300 V. Turn on the *Spectrometer* by clicking on the red/green button and click the ***Visible/Full*** switch to view only the visible spectrum.

9. *Is this spectrum different than hydrogen? How many lines are present and what are their colors?* _____

10. *Determine the wavelength (in nm), the frequency (in 1/s) and the energy (in J) for the peak on the far right.*

	λ (nm)	ν (1/s)	Energy (J)
Line (far right)			

VCL 8-3: Emission Spectra for Sodium and Mercury

In the 1800s, scientists found that when a sample of gas was excited by an alternating electric field, light with only certain discrete wavelengths was emitted. This property allowed for the development of spectroscopic techniques that can be used in the identification and analysis of elements and compounds. Even though scientists found spectroscopy very useful, they could not explain why the spectrum was not continuous. The explanation of this was left to Niels Bohr, a Danish physicist, who first proposed that energy levels of electrons are quantized and that excited electrons can only fall to discrete energy levels. This assignment illustrates the measurements that helped Bohr develop his original quantum model, as well as some practical uses for this science by measuring the emission spectra for mercury and sodium. Mercury vapor is used in fluorescent lights and sodium vapor is used in street lighting.

1. Start *Virtual ChemLab* and select *Emission Spectra for Sodium and Mercury* from the list of assignments. The lab will open in the Quantum laboratory. A sample of gaseous sodium is on the lab bench in a sample tube and an alternating electric field of 300 V has been applied to cause the sodium gas to emit light. A spectrometer is on the right side of the lab bench and has been turned on. You can separate the light in an emission spectrum by using an optical prism or a diffraction grating. A spectrometer is an instrument designed to separate the emitted light into its component wavelengths. The detector window shows the output from the spectrometer.

2. Click on the ***Visible/Full*** switch in the detector window to change the output from the spectrometer to the visible spectrum. One spectral line is much more intense than all the others.

   What is the color and wavelength (in nm) of this line? (To determine the wavelength, move the cursor over the line and read the wavelength in the *x* field at the bottom of the detector window.)

   _____

   Astronomers are excited about cities changing from normal incandescent streetlights to sodium vapor streetlights because astronomers can easily filter out the peak at 589 nm and minimize light pollution. Incandescent lights emit light at all wavelengths and make filtering impractical.

3. To exchange gas samples, double-click or click and drag the *Electric Field* and place it on the stockroom counter, and double-click or click and drag the *Gas (Na)* sample tube and place it on the stockroom counter as well. You may have to click on the main laboratory window in order to move the items.

4. Enter the stockroom by clicking in the *Stockroom*. Click on the *Gases* samples on the top shelf. Click on the cylinder labeled *Hg* to replace the Na in the sample tube with mercury vapor. If you point to the gas sample tube with the cursor it should read *Hg*.

5. Return to the laboratory and drag the gas sample tube off the stockroom counter and place it in the middle of the table as indicated by the spotlight. Drag the *Electric Field* and place it on the gas sample tube. Carefully click the button just above the left zero on the *Electric Field* controller and change the voltage to 300 V. Turn on the *Spectrometer* by clicking on the red/green button.

6. *How does the spectrum for mercury look different from sodium?* _____

   _____

Mercury vapor is used in the fluorescent light tubes that you see at school and home. The emitted light is not very bright for just the mercury vapor, but when scientists examined the full spectrum for mercury they saw what you just observed. There is an enormous emission in the ultraviolet region (UV). This light is sometimes called black light. You may have seen it with glow-in-the-dark displays.

Scientists coat the inside of the glass tube of fluorescent light tubes with a compound that will absorb UV and emit the energy as visible light with all the colors of the visible spectrum. All colors together create white light, which is why fluorescent light tubes emit very white light.

Laundry detergents contain compounds that absorb UV light and emit visible light. These compounds allow advertisers to claim *whiter and brighter whites and colors*. If you attend an event using black light, you may have seen your white socks or white shirt "glow."

VCL 8-4: Blackbody Radiation

In the early 1900s several experimental results appeared to be in conflict with classical physics. One of these experiments was the study of blackbody radiation. A blackbody is a solid (such as a piece of iron) that does not emit light at low temperatures, but, when heated, the "blackbody" begins to emit first red and then orange light and at higher temperatures eventually becomes white hot. The intensity of the emitted light is also a function of temperature. In this problem you will make observations similar to those of Max Planck (1858-1947) who, through his study of blackbody radiation, found an explanation that revolutionized how scientists think about radiated energy.

1. Start *Virtual ChemLab* and select *Blackbody Radiation* from the list of assignments. The lab will open in the Quantum laboratory. A metal sample holder with tungsten metal will be on the lab bench with an electric heater set at a temperature of 3000 K. A spectrometer is on the right and is switched on (the spectrometer window is open). Locate the switch that changes the display from wavelength to frequency and the switch that displays either the full electromagnetic spectrum or just the visible spectrum. These will be used later.

2. The spectrometer detects the intensity of the emitted light as a function of the wavelength (or frequency). In the grid below draw the spectrum detected by the spectrometer with wavelength (in nm) on the *x*-axis and intensity on the *y*-axis. If you drag your cursor over a peak, it will identify the wavelength (in nm) in the *x*-coordinate field in the bottom right corner of the detector window. Record the wavelength of the peak in the data table on the following page. (Round to whole numbers.)

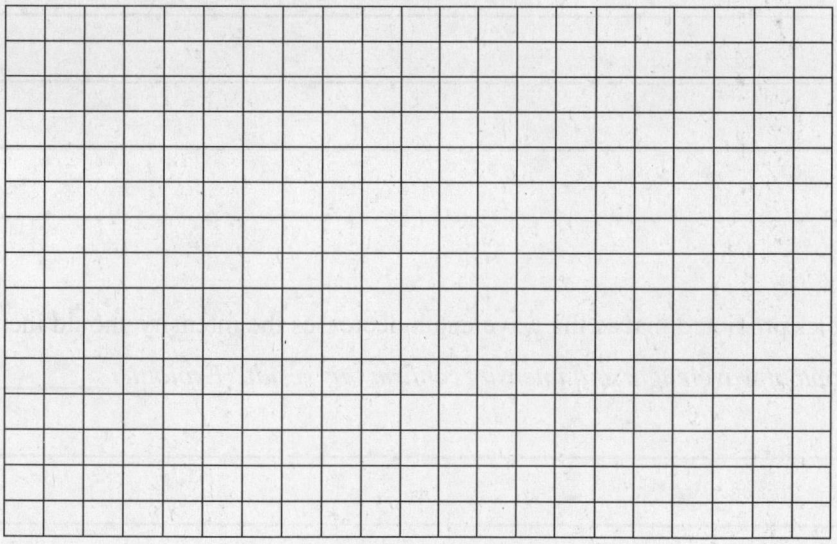

3. Change the temperature on the heater to 3100 K by clicking on the button above the hundreds place on the heater LCD controller. Record the shape of the curve on the same graph (label each line with a temperature) and the wavelength of the peak intensity in the data table. Continue with temperatures of 3200 K, 3300 K, 3400 K, 3500 K, and 3600 K. If you raise the temperature to 3700 K you will have to start over by clicking on the *Reset Lab* button just under the Danger sign, entering the *Stockroom*, clicking on the clipboard and selecting Preset Experiment #3 Blackbody Radiation.

Data Table

Temperature (K)	Wavelength (nm)
3000	
3100	
3200	
3300	
3400	
3500	
3600	

What observations can you make about the shape of the curve as temperature changes?

_____

_____

4. The visible portion of the electromagnetic spectrum occurs between 400 nm and 700 nm. Mark the visible spectrum on your graph.
Does the peak intensity ever occur in the visible region? Does this mean that there is no visible light radiated over this temperature range? Explain. _____

_____

_____

_____

_____

5. Classical physics predicted that as the wavelength decreases the intensity should increase.
Does your graph of wavelength and intensity confirm this result? Explain. _____

_____

_____

6. In the spectrometer window, change the display from wavelength to frequency.
What observations can you make about the magnitude of the intensity as the temperature is lowered from 3600 K to 3000 K by increments of 100 K? _____

_____

7. Change the temperature to 3700 K while observing the tungsten foil.

   What occurs at 3700 K? _____

8. This disparity between classical theory and experimental results was known as the "ultraviolet catastrophe." Classical physics predicted that the curve should continue to infinity as the wavelength is decreased. The conflicting experimental data required an innovative explanation. This explanation was provided by Max Planck who stated that the energy given off by the vibrating heated atoms was *quantized* and only vibrations of specific energy could occur. The quantized energy must be a multiple of $h\nu$ where h is known as Planck's constant (6.626×10^{-34} J·s) and ν is the frequency of the light in 1/s or s^{-1}. Calculate the energy of the peak intensity at 3400 K.

   Use the wavelength from the data table for 3400 K to determine first the frequency ($\nu = c/\lambda$, where c = speed of light = 2.998×10^8 $m \cdot s^{-1}$ and λ is the wavelength in meters) and then find the energy using $E = h\nu$.

VCL 8-5: Photoelectric Effect

Although Albert Einstein is most famous for $E = mc^2$ and for his work describing relativity in mechanics, his Nobel Prize was for understanding a very simple experiment. It was long understood that if you directed light of a certain wavelength at a piece of metal, it would emit electrons. In classical theory, the energy of the light was thought to be based on its intensity and not its frequency. However, the results of the photoelectric effect contradicted classical theory. Inconsistencies led Einstein to suggest that we need to think of light as being composed of particles (photons) and not just as waves. In this experiment, you will reproduce a photoelectric experiment and show that the energy (E) of a photon of light is related to its frequency and not its intensity.

1. Start *Virtual ChemLab* and select *Photoelectric Effect* from the list of assignments. The lab will open in the Quantum laboratory.

2. *What source is used in this experiment and what does it do?* _____

   _____

   At what intensity is the laser set? _____

   At what wavelength is the laser set? _____

   Record the wavelength (in nm) in the data table on the following page. Calculate the frequency (in Hz) and the energy (in J) using $c = \lambda v$ and $E = hv$ where $c = 2.998 \times 10^8$ m·s^{-1} and $h = 6.626 \times 10^{-34}$ J·s. Also record the color of the light by clicking on the *Spectrum Chart* (just behind the laser); the marker indicates what color is represented by the wavelength selected.

   Which metal foil is used in this experiment? _____

   What detector is used in this experiment and what does it measure? _____

   _____

   Turn on the detector by clicking on the red/green light switch.

   What does the signal on the phosphor screen indicate about the laser light shining on the sodium foil? _____

3. *Decrease the Intensity to 1 photon/second, how does the signal change?* _____

   _____

   Increase the Intensity to 1kW, how does the signal change? _____

   _____

   Change the *Intensity* back to 1 nW and increase the *Wavelength* to 600 nm.

   What do you observe? Record the wavelength in the data table. _____

Determine the maximum wavelength at which emission of electrons occurs in the metal. _____

What is the difference between intensity and wavelength? _____

_____

Which matters in the formation of photoelectrons: intensity or wavelength? _____

_____

Data Table

wavelength (nm)	frequency (1/s)	energy (J)	light color

4. Click inside the *Stockroom* to enter the stockroom. Click on the clipboard and select the preset experiment *Photoelectric Effect (2)*. Click on the green *Return to Lab* arrow to return to the laboratory. The intensity of the laser will be set at 1 nW and the wavelength at 400 nm. The detector used in this experiment is a bolometer and will be automatically turned on. This instrument measures the kinetic energy of electrons. You should see a green peak on the bolometer detection screen. The intensity or height of the signal corresponds to the number of electrons being emitted from the metal, and the *x*-axis is the kinetic energy of the electrons. Zoom in on the peak by clicking and dragging from the left of the peak to the right.

5. *Increase and decrease the Intensity, what do you observe?* _____

_____

Increase and decrease the Wavelength, what do you observe? _____

_____

_____

What is the maximum wavelength that ejects electrons from the sodium metal? _____

Based on this experiment, explain why violet light causes photoemission of electrons but orange light does not. _____

_____

VCL 8-6: The Rydberg Equation

When a sample of gas is excited by applying a large alternating electric field, the gas emits light at certain discrete wavelengths. In the late 1800s two scientists, Johann Balmer and Johannes Rydberg, developed an emperical equation that correlated the wavelength of the emitted light for certain gases such as H_2. Later, Niels Bohr's concept of quantized "jumps" by electrons between orbits was shown to be consistent with the Rydberg equation. In this assignment, you will measure the wavelengths of the lines in the hydrogen emission spectra and then graphically determine the value of the Rydberg constant, R_H.

1. Start *Virtual ChemLab* and select *The Rydberg Equation* from the list of assignments. The lab will open in the Quantum laboratory. The *Spectrometer* will be on the right of the lab table. The hydrogen emission spectra will be in the detector window in the upper right corner as a graph of intensity vs. wavelength (λ).

2. *How many distinct lines do you see and what are their colors?* _____

_____

3. Click on the ***Visible/Full*** switch to magnify only the visible spectrum. You will see four peaks in the spectrum. If you drag your cursor over a peak, it will identify the wavelength (in nm) in the *x*-coordinate field in the bottom right corner of the detector window. Record the wavelengths of the four peaks in the visible hydrogen spectrum in the data table. (Round to whole numbers.)

4. The Rydberg equation has the form $\frac{1}{\lambda} = R_H\left(\frac{1}{n_f^2} - \frac{1}{n_i^2}\right)$ where λ is the wavelength in meters, R_H is the Rydberg constant, n_f is the final principal quantum (for the Balmer series, which is in the visible spectrum, $n_f = 2$), and n_i is the initial principal quantum number ($n = 3, 4, 5, 6, \ldots$). Calculate from your experimental data the wavelength in meters and $1/\lambda$ in m^{-1}. Record your answers in the data table.

Data Table

	λ (nm)	λ (m)	$1/\lambda$ (m^{-1})
Line #1 (left)			
Line #2			
Line #3			
Line #4 (right)			

5. The formula for the determination of energy is $E = h\nu = hc/\lambda$ where h is Planck's constant and c is the speed of light. *What is the relationship between wavelength and energy?*

_____

6. *Of the four measured hydrogen spectrum lines recorded on the previous page, which line corresponds to the transition n = 3 to n = 2, and from n = 4 to n = 2, and so on from n = 6 to n = 2?*

_____

_____

_____

7. Calculate the value of $\left(\frac{1}{n_f^2} - \frac{1}{n_i^2}\right)$ for the transitions $n = 6$ to $n = 2$, $n = 5$ to $n = 2$, $n = 4$ to $n = 2$ and $n = 3$ to $n = 2$. Match the values for these transitions and record them with the appropriate reciprocal wavelength in the results table.

Results Table

Transition n_i to n_f	$\left(\frac{1}{n_f^2} - \frac{1}{n_i^2}\right)$	$1/\lambda$ (m^{-1})

8. The Rydberg equation, $\frac{1}{\lambda} = R_H\left(\frac{1}{n_f^2} - \frac{1}{n_i^2}\right)$, is in the form of $y = mx + b$ where $1/\lambda$ corresponds to y, $\left(\frac{1}{n_f^2} - \frac{1}{n_i^2}\right)$ corresponds to x, and $b = 0$. If you plot $1/\lambda$ on the y-axis and $\left(\frac{1}{n_f^2} - \frac{1}{n_i^2}\right)$ on the x-axis, the resulting slope will be the Rydberg constant, R_H.

Using a spreadsheet program or a piece of graph paper, plot your experimental data and determine the value of the Rydberg constant. _____

9. The accepted value for R_H is 1.0974×10^7 m^{-1}.

Determine the % error using the formula:

$$\%\,Error = \frac{|your\ answer - accepted\ answer|}{accepted\ answer} \times 100$$

$\%\,Error =$

VCL 8-7: Heisenberg Uncertainty Principle

It has long been known that if you shine light through narrow slits that are spaced at small intervals, the light will form a diffraction pattern. A diffraction pattern is a series of light and dark patterns caused by wave interference. The wave interference can be either constructive (light) or destructive (dark). In this experiment, you will shine a laser through a device with two slits where the spacing can be adjusted and then you will investigate the patterns that will be made at a distance from the slits.

1. Start *Virtual ChemLab* and select *Heisenberg Uncertainty Principle* from the list of assignments. The lab will open in the Quantum laboratory.

2. *What source is used in this experiment and for what reason?* _____

   _____

   At what wavelength is the laser set? _____

   What is the spacing of the two slits on the two-slit device? _____

   Sketch a small picture of the pattern displayed on the video screen.

3. Change the *Intensity* of the laser from 1 nW to 1W.

   Does the intensity of the light affect the diffraction pattern? _____

   Change the *Slit Spacing* to 1μm. Observe the pattern displayed on the video screen as you change the slit spacing from 1 μm to 7 μm in increments of 1μm.

   What can you state about the relationship between slit spacing and diffraction pattern?

   _____

4. Increase the *Wavelength* of the laser to 700 nm. _____

   What effect does an increase in the wavelength have on the diffraction pattern?

   _____

5. Decrease the *Intensity* on the laser to 1000 photons/second. Click on the ***Persist*** button on the video camera to look at individual photons coming through the slits. Observe for one minute.

   What observation can you make about this pattern compared with the pattern from the continuous beam of photons? _____

_____

Decrease the *Intensity* to 100 photons/second. Observe for another minute after clicking ***Persist***. At these lower intensities (1000 and 100 photons/second), there is never a time when two photons pass through the slits at the same time.

How can a single photon diffract?

_____

_____

_____

_____

Based on this experiment, what conclusions can you make about the nature of light?

_____

_____

6. Click inside the *Stockroom* to enter the stockroom. Click on the clipboard and select the preset experiment *Two-Slit Diffraction – Electrons*. Click on the green *Return to Lab* arrow to return to the laboratory.

What source is used in this experiment? _____

Sketch a small picture of the diffraction pattern shown on the Phosphor Screen.

How does this diffraction pattern compare with the diffraction pattern for light? _____

_____

Louis de Broglie was the first person to suggest that particles could be considered to have wave properties.

7. Decrease the *Intensity* to 10 electrons/second. The pattern now builds one electron at a time. Click on the ***Persist*** button and observe for one minute.

Has the diffraction pattern changed? Why or why not? _____

_____

How can a single electron diffract? _____

_____

_____

_____

When you look at the complete diffraction pattern of a stream of particles, you are seeing all the places you expect particles to scatter. If you start the source over multiple times, you will see that the first particle is never detected in the same place twice. This is an application of the Heisenberg Uncertainty Principle, which is directly connected with measurement. It takes into account the minimum uncertainty of the position (Δx) and the uncertainty of the momentum (Δp) using the equation $(\Delta x)(\Delta p) \geq h/4\pi$. Because you know the energy at which the particle is traveling, you can precisely know the momentum, but you cannot know the position. Consequently, you cannot predict where each particle will hit.

VCL 12-1: Heat of Vaporization of Water

A graph of the vapor pressure of a liquid as a function of temperature has a characteristic shape that can be represented fairly accurately with the *Clausius-Clapeyron* equation. In this assignment you will measure the vapor pressure of water at several temperatures and then use this data to estimate the heat of vaporization of water using the *Clausius-Clapeyron* equation.

1. Start *Virtual ChemLab* and select *Heat of Vaporization of Water* from the list of assignments. The lab will open in the Gases laboratory.

2. The balloon is filled with 0.10 moles of water vapor at a pressure of 140 kPa and a temperature of 400 K. Pull down the lever on the Temperature LCD controller until the temperature stops decreasing. This temperature represents the equilibrium temperature where water as a gas exists in equilibrium with water as a liquid. The pressure at this temperature is the vapor pressure. Record the vapor pressure (in kPa) and the temperature (in K) in the data table.

3. Change the pressure from 140 kPa to 120 kPa using the lever on the Pressure LCD controller or by clicking on the tens place and typing "2." Pull down the lever on the Temperature controller until the temperature stops decreasing. Record the vapor pressure (in kPa) and the temperature (in K) in the data table. Continue this process with pressures of 100 kPa, 80 kPa, 60 kPa, and 40 kPa. Do not forget to decrease the temperature until the temperature stops decreasing after each pressure change. Record all vapor pressure and temperatures in the data table.

Data Table

Vapor Pressure (kPa)	Temperature (K)

4. The *Clausius-Clapeyron* equation has the form $\ln\frac{P_2}{P_1} = -\frac{\Delta H_{vap}}{R}\left(\frac{1}{T_2} - \frac{1}{T_1}\right)$. If you plot ln *P* (natural log of the vapor pressure) as a function of $1/T$, the data should form a straight line. Using a spreadsheet program and the data you collected, plot $1/T$ (reciprocal temperature) on the *x*-axis and ln *P* (natural log of the vapor pressure) on the *y*-axis.

   Describe the curve. _____

5. Graphically or using the spreadsheet program, determine the best linear fit for your curve and find the slope of the line. From the *Clausius-Clapeyron* equation, ΔH_{vap} = -slope × *R* where *R* = 8.314 $J \cdot K^{-1} \cdot mol^{-1}$.

   Based on your slope, calculate the heat of vaporization of water in kJ/mol.

   _____

6. The accepted value for the heat of vaporization of water is 40.7 kJ/mol.

Calculate the percent error using the formula:

$$\%\ Error = \frac{|your\ answer - accepted\ answer|}{accepted\ answer} \times 100$$

$$\%\ Error =$$

VCL 12-2: The Boiling Point of Water at High Altitude

The relationship between the equilibrium vapor pressure of a liquid or solid and temperature is given by the *Clausius-Clapeyron* equation. In this assignment you will measure the vapor pressure of water at a given temperature and use this data and the *Clausius-Clapeyron* equation to calculate the boiling point of water on the top of Mt. Denali in Alaska.

1. Start *Virtual ChemLab* and select *The Boiling Point of Water at High Altitude* from the list of assignments. The lab will open in the Gases laboratory.

2. The balloon is filled with 0.40 moles of water vapor at a pressure of 1500 Torr and a temperature of 400 K. Pull down the lever on the Temperature LCD controller until the temperature stops decreasing. This temperature represents the equilibrium temperature where water as a gas exists in equilibrium with water as a liquid. The pressure at this temperature is the vapor pressure. Record the vapor pressure (in Torr) and the temperature (in K) in the data table.

Data Table

Vapor Pressure (Torr)	Temperature (K)

3. The *Clausius-Clapeyron* equation may be written in several forms. For this assignment, the most useful form can be written as

$$\ln\frac{P_2}{P_1} = -\frac{\Delta H_{\text{vap}}}{R}\left(\frac{1}{T_2} - \frac{1}{T_1}\right)$$

If P_1 and T_1 are the experimental vapor pressure and temperature that you measured and the pressure at the top of Mt. Denali, P_2, is 340 Torr, the boiling point of water, T_2, at the top of the mountain can be calculated by solving the *Clausius-Clapeyron* equation for T_2.

Calculate the boiling point of water at the top of Mt. Denali. The value of R is 8.314 $J \cdot K^{-1} \cdot mol^{-1}$ and ΔH_{vap} for water is 40.67 kJ/mol

VCL 12-3: Heat of Fusion of Water

The molar heat of fusion for a substance, ΔH_{fus}, is the heat required to transform one mole of the substance from the solid phase into the liquid phase. In this assignment, you will use a simple coffee cup calorimeter and a thermometer to measure the molar heat of fusion for water.

1. Start *Virtual ChemLab* and select *Heat of Fusion of Water* from the list of assignments. The lab will open in the Calorimetry laboratory with a beaker of ice on the balance and a coffee cup calorimeter on the lab bench.

2. Click on the *Lab Book* to open it. Record the mass of the ice on the balance in the data table. If the mass is too small to read, click on the *Balance* area to zoom in. Note that the balance has already been tared for the mass of the empty beaker.

3. 100 mL of water is already in the coffee cup. Use the density of water at 25°C (0.998 g/mL) to determine the mass of water from the volume. Record the mass in the data table. Make certain the stirrer is ***On*** (you should be able to see the shaft rotating). Click the thermometer window to bring it to the front and click ***Save*** to begin recording data to the lab book. Allow 20-30 seconds to obtain a baseline temperature of the water.

4. Drag the beaker from the balance area until it snaps into place above the coffee cup and then pour the ice into the calorimeter. Click the thermometer and graph windows to bring them to the front again and observe the change in temperature in the graph window until it reaches a minimum value and begins to warm again. Click ***Stop*** in the temperature window. (You can click on the clock on the wall labeled *Accelerate* to accelerate the time in the laboratory.) A blue data link will appear in the lab book. Click the blue data link and record the temperature before adding the ice and the *lowest* temperature after adding ice in the data table. (Remember that the water will begin to warm back up after all of the ice has melted.)

5. If you want to repeat the experiment, click on the red disposal bucket to clear the lab, click on the Stockroom, click on the clipboard, and select Preset Experiment #3, Heat of Fusion of Water.

Data Table

volume of water in calorimeter (mL)	
mass of water in calorimeter (g)	
mass of ice (g)	
initial temperature (°C)	
final temperature (°C)	

6. *Calculate ΔT for the water using $\Delta T = |T_f - T_i|$.* _____

7. *Calculate the heat (q) transferred, in kJ, from the water to the ice using $q = m \times C \times \Delta T$ where the heat capacity (C) for water is 4.18 J/K·g and the mass, m, is for the water in the calorimeter.*

_____

8. *Convert the mass of ice to moles.* _____

9. *Calculate ΔH_{fus} of water, in kJ/mol, by dividing the heat transferred from the water by the moles of ice melted.* _____

10. *Compare your experimental value of ΔH_{fus} of ice with the accepted value of 6.01 kJ/mol and calculate the % error using the formula:*

$$\%\ Error = \frac{|your\ answer - accepted\ answer|}{accepted\ answer} \times 100$$

$$\%\ Error =$$

11. *What are some possible sources of error in this laboratory procedure?* _____

_____

_____

_____

VCL 13-1: Creating a Solution of Known Molarity

In this assignment, you will weigh out a sample of baking soda ($NaHCO_3$) and create a solution of known molarity.

1. Start *Virtual ChemLab* and select *Creating a Solution of Known Molarity* from the list of assignments. The lab will open in the Titration laboratory.

2. In the laboratory, a bottle of baking soda (sodium bicarbonate, $NaHCO_3$) will be next to the balance, and an empty beaker will be on the stir plate. Drag the empty beaker to the spotlight next to the balance, click in the *Balance* area to zoom in, place a weigh paper on the balance, and tare the balance.

3. Open the bottle by clicking on the lid (*Remove Lid*). Pick up the *Scoop* and scoop out some sample by first dragging the scoop to the mouth of the bottle and then pulling the scoop down the face of the bottle. As the scoop is dragged down the face of the bottle it will pick up different quantities of solid. Select the largest sample possible and drag the scoop to the weighing paper on the balance until it snaps in place and then let go. This will put approximately 1 g of sample on the balance. Repeat with a second *Scoop*. Record the mass of the $NaHCO_3$ in the data table.

4. Drag the weigh paper to the beaker and add the $NaHCO_3$ sample to the beaker. Click on the green *Zoom Out* arrow to return to the laboratory.

5. Drag the beaker to the 50 mL graduated cylinder (the largest one) by the sink and empty the sample into the cylinder. Hold the cylinder under the tap until it fills with water to make an aqueous solution of $NaHCO_3$. (When the graduated cylinder is full it will automatically snap back into place.) Note that the solid is added and dissolved before the volume is measured when making a molar solution. Chemists normally use a volumetric flask for making molar solutions, but this is not available in the simulation.

6. *Determine the liters of solution in the cylinder and record the data in the data table.*

7. *Determine the moles of $NaHCO_3$ in the sample and record the data in the data table.*

Data Table

mass $NaHCO_3$	
moles $NaHCO_3$	
liters solution	

8. The molarity is calculated using the formula:

$$\text{molarity} = \frac{\text{moles solute}}{\text{L solution}} = \frac{\text{mass solute}/\text{molar mass solute}}{\text{L solution}}$$

Calculate the molarity of the $NaHCO_3$ solution in units of mol/L.

VCL 13-2: Creating a Solution of Known Molality

In this assignment, you will weigh out a sample of solid NH_4Cl and create a solution of known molality.

1. Start *Virtual ChemLab* and select *Creating a Solution of Known Molality* from the list of assignments. The lab will open in the Titration laboratory.

2. In the laboratory, a bottle of ammonium chloride (NH_4Cl) will be next to the balance and an empty beaker will be on the stir plate. Drag the beaker to the spotlight next to the balance, and click in the balance area to zoom in. Place the beaker on the balance and tare the balance. Click on the green *Zoom Out* arrow to return to the laboratory.

3. Drag the beaker to the sink and fill it with water until the beaker is approximately one-quarter full. Return the beaker to the balance and click in the *Balance* area to zoom in. Record the mass of the water in the data table. Drag the beaker off the balance to the spotlight on the right.

4. Place a weigh paper on the balance and tare the balance. Open the bottle by clicking on the lid (*Remove Lid*). Pick up the *Scoop* and scoop out some sample by first dragging the scoop to the mouth of the bottle and then pulling the scoop down the face of the bottle. As the scoop is dragged down the face of the bottle it will pick up different quantities of solid. Select the largest sample possible and drag the scoop to the weighing paper on the balance until it snaps in place and then let go. This will put approximately 1 g of sample on the balance. Repeat with a second *Scoop*. Record the mass of the NH_4Cl in the data table.

5. Drag the weigh paper to the beaker of water and add the NH_4Cl sample to the water to make an aqueous solution of NH_4Cl.

6. *Determine the kilograms of solvent (water) in the beaker and record the data in the data table.*

7. *Determine the moles of NH_4Cl in the sample and record the data in the data table.*

Data Table

mass NH_4Cl	
moles NH_4Cl	
mass water	
kg water	

8. The molality is calculated using the formula:

$$\text{molality} = \frac{\text{moles solute}}{\text{kg solvent}} = \frac{\text{mass solute}/\text{molar mass solute}}{\text{kg solvent}}$$

Calculate the molality of the NH_4Cl solution in units of mol/kg.

VCL 13-3: Converting Concentrations to Different Units

Occasionally, when making solutions in the laboratory, it is convenient to make a solution with a certain concentration unit, such as molarity, and then convert the concentration to a different unit. In this assignment, you will make a sodium bicarbonate (baking soda) solution of a certain molarity and then convert that concentration to molality, mass percent, and mole fraction.

1. Start *Virtual ChemLab* and select *Converting Concentrations to Different Units* from the list of assignments. The lab will open in the Titration laboratory.

2. In the laboratory, a bottle of baking soda (sodium bicarbonate, $NaHCO_3$) will be next to the balance, and an empty beaker will be on the stir plate. Drag the empty beaker to the spotlight next to the balance, click in the *Balance* area to zoom in, place a weigh paper on the balance, and tare the balance.

3. Open the bottle by clicking on the lid (*Remove Lid*). Pick up the *Scoop* and scoop out some sample by first dragging the scoop to the mouth of the bottle and then pulling the scoop down the face of the bottle. As the scoop is dragged down the face of the bottle, it will pick up different quantities of solid. Select the largest sample possible and drag the scoop to the weighing paper on the balance until it snaps in place and then let go. This will put approximately 1 g of sample on the balance. Repeat this process six additional times so there is approximately 7.0 g of sample. Record the mass of the $NaHCO_3$ in the data table.

4. Drag the weigh paper to the beaker and add the $NaHCO_3$ sample to the beaker. Click on the green *Zoom Out* arrow to return to the laboratory.

5. Drag the beaker to the 50 mL graduated cylinder (the largest one) by the sink and empty the sample into the cylinder. Hold the cylinder under the tap until it fills with water to make an aqueous solution of $NaHCO_3$. (When the graduated cylinder is full, it will automatically snap back into place.) Note that the solid is added and dissolved before the volume is measured when making a molar solution. Chemists normally use a volumetric flask for making molar solutions, but this is not available in the simulation. Record the volume of the solution, in L, in the data table.

6. *Calculate the moles of $NaHCO_3$ in the sample and record the data in the data table.*

Data Table

mass $NaHCO_3$	
moles $NaHCO_3$	
liters $NaHCO_3$	

7. The molarity is calculated using the formula:

$$\text{molarity} = \frac{\text{moles solute}}{\text{L solution}} = \frac{\text{mass solute}/\text{molar mass solute}}{\text{L solution}}$$

Calculate the molarity of the $NaHCO_3$ solution in units of mol/L.

8. *If the density of the solution is 1.047 g/mL, calculate the molality of the solution in units of mol/kg.*

9. *Calculate the mass percent of sodium bicarbonate in the solution.*

10. *Calculate the mole fraction of sodium bicarbonate in the solution.*

VCL 13-4: Enthalpy of Solution: NH_4NO_3

Have you ever used one of those "instant cold packs" that looks like a plastic bag filled with liquid? If you hit the bag and shake it up it gets extremely cold, but why does it do that? The liquid inside the cold pack is water, and in the water is another plastic bag or tube containing NH_4NO_3 fertilizer. When you hit the cold pack, it breaks the tube so that the water mixes with the fertilizer. The dissolving of a salt, such as NH_4NO_3, in water is called dissolution, and the heat associated with the dissolving process is called the Enthalpy of Solution. In this problem, you will take a sample of NH_4NO_3, dissolve it in water, and after measuring the change in temperature, calculate the enthalpy of solution for NH_4NO_3.

1. Start *Virtual ChemLab* and select *Enthalpy of Solution: NH_4NO_3* from the list of assignments. The lab will open in the Calorimetry laboratory.

2. There will be a bottle of ammonium nitrate (NH_4NO_3) on the lab bench. A weigh paper will be on the balance with approximately 2 g of NH_4NO_3 on the paper. Record the mass of the sample in the data table. If you cannot read the mass on the balance, click in the balance area to *Zoom In. Return to Lab* when you have recorded the mass.

3. The coffee cup calorimeter will be on the lab bench and filled with 100 mL water. Click the *Lab Book* to open it. Make certain the stirrer is ***On*** (you should be able to see the shaft rotating). In the thermometer window click ***Save*** to begin recording data. Allow 20-30 seconds to obtain a baseline temperature of the water.

4. Drag the weigh paper with the sample to the calorimeter until it snaps into place and then pour the sample into the calorimeter. Observe the change in temperature until it reaches a maximum and then record data for an additional 20-30 seconds. Click ***Stop***. (You can click on the clock on the wall labeled *Accelerate* to accelerate the time in the laboratory.) A blue data link will appear in the lab book. Click the data link and record the temperature before adding the NH_4NO_3 and the *highest* or *lowest* temperature after adding the NH_4NO_3 in the data table.

Data Table

Mixture	mass	$T_{initial}$	T_{final}
NH_4NO_3 (s) + H_2O (l)			

5. *Calculate ΔT ($\Delta T = T_{initial} - T_{final}$) for the dissolving process.* _____

6. An exothermic process gives off heat (warms up), and an endothermic process absorbs heat (cools off).

   Was the addition of NH_4NO_3 to the water an endothermic or exothermic process? What is the sign of the change in enthalpy (ΔH)? _____

7. *Determine the moles of NH_4NO_3 in the sample.* The molecular weight of NH_4NO_3 is 80 g/mol.

8. The heat absorbed or lost by the water can be calculated using $q = m \cdot C_{\text{water}} \cdot \Delta T$. Assume that the density of water is 1 g/mL.

   Calculate the mass of the water and substitute for m. ΔT is the change in the temperature of the water and C_{water} is the specific heat capacity for water (4.184 J/g·K). What is the heat absorbed or lost, in J, by the water? _____

9. The heat transferred from/to the NH_4NO_3 can be divided by the moles of NH_4NO_3 to obtain the molar heat of solution for NH_4NO_3.

   What is the molar heat of solution, in kJ, of NH_4NO_3? _____

   _____

10. *If the accepted value for the heat of solution for sugar is 25.69 kJ/mol, calculate the percent error.*

$$\%\ Error = \frac{|your\ answer - accepted\ answer|}{accepted\ answer} \times 100$$

$$\%\ Error =$$

This experiment does not consider that all of the conditions are standard state conditions; therefore, you are calculating ΔH_{sol} **not** ΔH°_{sol}.

VCL 13-5: Freezing Point Depression

If you dissolve a substance such as ordinary table salt (NaCl) in water, the freezing point of the water will decrease relative to the freezing point of the pure water. This property is used to melt the snow or ice on roads during the winter or to make homemade ice cream. In this assignment, you will dissolve a sample of NaCl in water, add some ice, and then measure the freezing point depression.

1. Start *Virtual ChemLab* and select *Freezing Point Depression* from the list of assignments. The lab will open in the Calorimetry laboratory with a beaker containing 45.00 g of ice and a coffee cup calorimeter on the lab bench. A sample of sodium chloride (NaCl) will also be on the balance.

2. Click on the *Lab Book* to open it. Record the mass of the sodium chloride in the data table. If it is too small to read, click on the *Balance* area to zoom in, record the mass, and then return to the laboratory.

3. 100 mL of water is already in the calorimeter. Use the density of water at 25°C (0.998 g/mL) to determine the mass from the volume and record it in the data table. Make certain the stirrer is ***On*** (you should be able to see the shaft rotating). Click the thermometer window to bring it to the front and click ***Save*** to begin recording data in the lab book. Allow 20-30 seconds to obtain a baseline temperature of the water. Click the clock on the wall labeled *Accelerate* to accelerate the laboratory time if necessary.

4. Drag the beaker of ice until it snaps into place above the calorimeter and then pour the ice into the calorimeter. Click the thermometer and graph windows to bring them to the front again and observe the change in temperature in the graph window until it reaches zero. Drag the weigh paper from the balance to the calorimeter and then pour it into the calorimeter. Observe the change in temperature until it reaches a stable minimum and click ***Stop*** in the temperature window. A blue data link will appear in the lab book. Click the blue data link and record the *lowest* temperature after adding the salt in the data table. (Remember that the water may have begun to warm back up.)

5. If you want to repeat the experiment, click on the red disposal bucket to clear the lab, click on the Stockroom, click on the clipboard, and select Preset Experiment #1, Freezing Point Depression – NaCl.

Data Table

mass NaCl	
mass water	
mass ice	
mass water + ice	
minimum temperature	

6. The freezing point depression can be predicted using the equation $\Delta T = K_f \times m \times i$, where ΔT is the change in freezing point, i is the number of ions in the solution per mole of dissolved NaCl ($i = 2$), m is the molality of the solution, and K_f is the molal freezing point constant for water which is 1.86°C/m.

Calculate the predicted change in freezing point for your solution.

7. The change in freezing point must be subtracted from the freezing point of pure water, which is 0.0 °C, in order to compare the predicted freezing point with the actual freezing point.

What is the calculated freezing point of the solution? Compare this to the actual freezing point.

_____

VCL 13-6: Boiling Point Elevation

If you dissolve a substance such as ordinary table salt (NaCl) in water, the boiling point of the water will increase relative to the boiling point of the pure water. In this assignment, you will dissolve a sample of NaCl in water and then measure the boiling point elevation for the solution.

1. Start *Virtual ChemLab* and select *Boiling Point Elevation* from the list of assignments. The lab will open in the Calorimetry laboratory with a calorimeter on the lab bench and a sample of sodium chloride (NaCl) on the balance.

2. Record the mass of the sodium chloride in the data table. If it is too small to read, click on the *Balance* area to zoom in, record the reading, and then return to the laboratory.

3. 100 mL of water is already in the calorimeter. Use the density of water at 25°C (0.998 g/mL) to determine the mass from the volume and record it in the data table. Make certain the stirrer is ***On*** (you should be able to see the shaft rotating). Click on the green heater light on the control panel to turn on the heater and begin heating the water. Click the clock on the wall labeled *Accelerate* to accelerate the laboratory time if necessary.

4. Observe the temperature until the first appearance of steam comes from the calorimeter. Immediately click the red light on the heater to turn it off and then record the temperature as the boiling point of pure water in the data table. Letting the water boil will decrease the mass of the water present in the calorimeter. Note that the boiling point may be different than 100°C if the atmospheric pressure is *not* 760 Torr. The current atmospheric pressure for the day can be checked by selecting *Pressure* on the LED meter on the wall.

5. Drag the weigh paper to the calorimeter and add the NaCl. Wait 30 seconds for the salt to dissolve and then turn on the heater. When steam first appears observe and record the temperature in the data table.

6. If you want to repeat the experiment, click on the red disposal bucket to clear the lab, click on the Stockroom, click on the clipboard, and select Preset Experiment #2, Boiling Point Elevation – NaCl.

Data Table

mass NaCl	
mass water	
boiling temp of pure water	
boiling temp of solution	

7. The boiling point elevation can be predicted using the equation $\Delta T = K_b \times m \times i$, where ΔT is the change in boiling point, i is the number of ions in the solution per mole of dissolved NaCl ($i = 2$), m is the molality of the solution, and K_b is the molal boiling point constant for water which is 0.51°C/m.

   Calculate the predicted change in boiling point, in °C for your solution.

8. The change in boiling point must be added to the boiling point of pure water in your experiment in order to compare the predicted boiling point with the actual boiling point.

What is the calculated boiling point of the solution? Compare this with the actual boiling point.

VCL 13-7: Molar Mass Determination by Freezing Point Depression

If you dissolve a substance such as ordinary table salt (NaCl) in water, the freezing point of the water will decrease relative to the freezing point of the pure water. You can use this property to calculate the molar mass of an unknown. In this assignment, you will dissolve a sample of NaCl in water, measure the freezing point depression for the solution, and then calculate the molar mass for NaCl as if it were an unknown.

1. Start *Virtual ChemLab* and select *Freezing Point Depression* from the list of assignments. The lab will open in the Calorimetry laboratory with a beaker containing 45.00 g of ice and a coffee cup calorimeter on the lab bench. A sample of sodium chloride (NaCl) will also be on the balance.

2. Click on the *Lab Book* to open it. Record the mass of the sodium chloride in the data table. If it is too small to read, click on the *Balance* area to zoom in, record the mass, and then return to the laboratory.

3. 100 mL of water is already in the calorimeter. Use the density of water at 25°C (0.998 g/mL) to determine the mass from the volume and record it in the data table. Make certain the stirrer is ***On*** (you should be able to see the shaft rotating). Click the thermometer window to bring it to the front and click ***Save*** to begin recording data in the lab book. Allow 20-30 seconds to obtain a baseline temperature of the water. Click the clock on the wall labeled *Accelerate* to accelerate the laboratory time if necessary.

4. Drag the beaker of ice until it snaps into place above the calorimeter and then pour the ice into the calorimeter. Click the thermometer and graph windows to bring them to the front again and observe the change in temperature in the graph window until it reaches zero. Drag the weigh paper from the balance to the calorimeter and then pour it into the calorimeter. Observe the change in temperature until it reaches a stable minimum and click ***Stop*** in the temperature window. A blue data link will appear in the lab book. Click the blue data link and record the *lowest* temperature after adding the salt in the data table. (Remember that the water may have begun to warm back up.)

5. If you want to repeat the experiment, click on the red disposal bucket to clear the lab, click on the Stockroom, click on the clipboard, and select Preset Experiment #1, Freezing Point Depression – NaCl.

Data Table

mass NaCl	
mass water	
mass ice	
mass water + ice	
minimum temperature	

6. *What is the freezing point depression caused by adding NaCl to the water?* _____

7. The freezing point depression can be calculated using the equation $\Delta T = K_f \times m \times i$, where ΔT is the change in freezing point, i is the number of ions in the solution per mole of dissolved NaCl ($i = 2$), m is the molality of the solution, and K_f is the molal freezing point constant for water which is 1.86°C/m.

Using this equation and the data recorded in the data table, calculate the molar mass for NaCl and compare it with the actual value.

VCL 13-8: Molar Mass Determination by Boiling Point Elevation

If you dissolve a substance such as ordinary table salt (NaCl) in water, the boiling point of the water will increase relative to the boiling point of the pure water. You can use this property to calculate the molar mass of an unknown. In this assignment, you will dissolve a sample of NaCl in water, measure the boiling point elevation for the solution, and then calculate the molar mass for NaCl as if it were an unknown.

1. Start *Virtual ChemLab* and select *Boiling Point Elevation* from the list of assignments. The lab will open in the Calorimetry laboratory with a calorimeter on the lab bench and a sample of sodium chloride (NaCl) on the balance.

2. Record the mass of the sodium chloride in the data table. If it is too small to read, click on the *Balance* area to zoom in, record the reading, and then return to the laboratory.

3. 100 mL of water is already in the calorimeter. Use the density of water at 25°C (0.998 g/mL) to determine the mass from the volume and record it in the data table. Make certain the stirrer is ***On*** (you should be able to see the shaft rotating). Click on the green heater light on the control panel to turn on the heater and begin heating the water. Click the clock on the wall labeled *Accelerate* to accelerate the laboratory time if necessary.

4. Observe the temperature until the first appearance of steam comes from the calorimeter. Immediately click the red light on the heater to turn it off and then record the temperature as the boiling point of pure water in the data table. Letting the water boil will decrease the mass of the water present in the calorimeter. Note that the boiling point may be different than 100°C if the atmospheric pressure is *not* 760 Torr. The current atmospheric pressure for the day can be checked by selecting *Pressure* on the LED meter on the wall.

5. Drag the weigh paper to the calorimeter and add the NaCl. Wait 30 seconds for the salt to dissolve and then turn on the heater. When steam first appears, observe and record the temperature in the data table.

6. If you want to repeat the experiment, click on the red disposal bucket to clear the lab, click on the Stockroom, click on the clipboard, and select Preset Experiment #2, Boiling Point Elevation – NaCl.

Data Table

mass NaCl	
mass water	
boiling temp of pure water	
boiling temp of solution	

7. *Calculate the boiling point elevation, ΔT, caused by adding NaCl to the water.*

_____

8. The boiling point elevation can be calculated using the equation $\Delta T = K_b \times m \times i$, where ΔT is the change in boiling point, i is the number of ions in the solution per mole of dissolved NaCl ($i = 2$), m is the molality of the solution, and K_b is the molal boiling point constant for water which is 0.51°C/m.

Using this equation and the data recorded in the data table, calculate the molar mass for NaCl and compare it with the actual value.

VCL: 13-9: Changes in the Boiling Point

If you dissolve a substance such as ordinary table salt (NaCl) in water, the boiling point of the water will increase relative to the boiling point of the pure water. In this assignment, you will dissolve a sample of NaCl in water and then observe what happens when you continue to boil the water until the water boils away.

1. Start *Virtual ChemLab* and select *Changes in the Boiling Point* from the list of assignments. The lab will open in the Calorimetry laboratory with a calorimeter on the lab bench and a sample of sodium chloride (NaCl) on the balance.

2. 100 mL of water is already in the calorimeter. Make certain the stirrer is ***On*** (you should be able to see the shaft rotating). Drag the weigh paper to the calorimeter and add the NaCl. Wait 30 seconds for the salt to dissolve and then turn on the heater by clicking on the green heater light on the control panel. Click the clock on the wall labeled *Accelerate* to accelerate the laboratory time if necessary.

3. When steam first appears, observe the temperature. Allow the solution to continue boiling and observe the temperature until all of the water boils away and the heater burns out. (The water level is shown on the right side of the calorimeter control panel.)

   What observations did you make about the temperature as the solution continued to boil?

   _____

4. *Explain the observations described in question # 3. Why does this occur?*

   _____

   _____

   _____

VCL 16-1: Ionization Constants of Weak Acids

An acid-base indicator is usually a weak acid with a characteristic color in the protonated and deprotonated forms. In this assignment, you will monitor the color of an acetic acid solution containing *Bromocresol Green* as an indicator, as the pH is changed and then you will estimate the ionization constant, K_a, for the indicator.

1. Start *Virtual ChemLab* and select *Ionization Constants of Weak Acids* from the list of assignments. The lab will open in the Titration laboratory. Bottles of 0.1104 M NaOH and 0.1031 M HAc (acetic acid) will be on the lab bench. The buret will be filled with the NaOH solution and a beaker containing 10.00 mL of the HAc solution will be on the stir plate. The stir plate will be on, *Bromocresol Green* indicator will have been added to the beaker, and a calibrated pH probe will also be in the beaker so the pH of the solution can be monitored.

2. *What is the color and pH of the solution?* _____

3. On the buret, the horizontal position of the orange handle is off for the stopcock. Open the stopcock by pulling down on the orange handle. The vertical position delivers solution the fastest with three intermediate rates in between (slow drop-wise, fast drop-wise, and slow stream). Turn the stopcock to the second position or fast drop-wise addition. Observe the color of the solution and close the stopcock when the color turns green by double clicking on the center of the stopcock.

4. *What is the color and pH of the solution now?* _____

5. Continue to add NaOH as before or at a faster rate.

   What is the final color of the solution? _____

6. An acid-base indicator is usually a weak acid with a characteristic color in the protonated and deprotonated forms. Because bromocresol green is an acid, it is convenient to represent its rather complex formula as HBCG. HBCG ionizes in water according to the following equation:

$$\underset{\text{(yellow)}}{HBCG} + H_2O = \underset{\text{(blue)}}{BCG^-} + H_3O^+$$

   The K_a (the equilibrium constant for the acid) expression is:

$$K_a = \frac{[BCG^-][H_3O^+]}{[HBCG]}$$

   When $[BCG^-] = [HBCG]$, then $K_a = [H_3O^+]$. If you know the pH of the solution, then the $[H_3O^+]$ and K_a can be determined.

   What would be the color of the solution if there were equal concentrations of HBCG and BCG^-?

   _____

7. *What is the pH at the first appearance of this color?* _____

_____

8. *What is an estimate for the K_a for bromocresol green?* _____

_____

VCL 16-2: Acid-Base Classification of Salts

In this assignment you will be asked to classify aqueous solutions of salts as to whether they are acidic, basic, or neutral. This is most easily done by first identifying how both the cation and anion affect the pH of the solution and then by combining the effects. After predicting the acid-base properties of these salts, you will then test your predictions in the laboratory.

1. *State whether 0.1 M solutions of each of the following salts are acidic, basic, or neutral. Explain your reasoning for each by writing a balanced net ionic equation to describe the behavior of each non-neutral salt in water: NaCN, KNO_3, NH_4Cl, $NaHCO_3$, and Na_3PO_4.*

   NaCN: _____

   KNO_3: _____

   NH_4Cl: _____

   $NaHCO_3$: _____

   Na_3PO_4: _____

Once you have predicted the nature of each salt solution, you will use *Virtual ChemLab* to confirm your prediction. Each solution must be approximately 0.1 M for your comparisons to be valid. Most of the solutions in the Stockroom are approximately 0.1 M already. Three solutions must be prepared from solid salts. One of these salt solutions is already prepared and on the lab bench ready for you to measure the pH.

2. Start *Virtual ChemLab* and select *Acid-Base Classification of Salts* from the list of assignments. The lab will open in the Titrations laboratory.

3. On the stir plate, there will be a beaker of 0.10 M ammonium chloride (NH_4Cl) that has already been prepared. The pH meter has been calibrated and is in the beaker. Record the pH of the NH_4Cl solution in the data table on the following page. When finished, drag the beaker to the red disposal bucket, and drag the bottle of NH_4Cl to the stockroom counter.

4. Click in the *Stockroom* to enter. Double-click on the NH_4Cl bottle to return it to the shelf and then double-click on the $NaHCO_3$ and KNO_3 bottles to move them to the *Stockroom* counter. Return to the laboratory.

5. Open the beaker drawer (click on it) and drag a beaker to the spotlight next to the *Balance*. Click and drag the bottle of $NaHCO_3$ and place it on the spot light near the balance. Click in the *Balance* area to zoom in. Place a weigh paper on the balance and tare the balance. Open the bottle by clicking on the lid (*Remove Lid*). Pick up the *Scoop* and scoop up some salt by dragging the *Scoop* to the mouth of the bottle and then down the face of the bottle. Each scoop position on the face of the bottle represents a different size scoop. Pull the scoop down from the top to the second position (approximately 0.20 g) and drag it to the weigh paper in the balance until it snaps into place. Releasing the scoop places the sample on the weigh paper. Now drag the weigh paper from the balance to the beaker until it snaps into place and then empty the salt into the beaker. Return to the laboratory and drag the beaker to the stir plate.

6. Drag the 25 mL graduated cylinder to the sink under the tap until it fills. When filled, it will return to the lab bench and will indicate that it is full when you place the cursor over the cylinder. Drag the 25 mL cylinder to the beaker on the stir plate and empty it into the beaker. Place the pH probe in the beaker and record the pH in the data table. Drag the beaker to the red disposal bucket. Double-click the bottle of $NaHCO_3$ to move it to the *Stockroom* counter. Repeat steps 5 and 6 for KNO_3.

7. Click in the *Stockroom*. The stock solutions of NaCN and Na_3PO_4 are already approximately 0.1 M. Double-click each bottle to move them to the counter and return to the laboratory. With these solutions you can pour a small amount into a beaker that you have placed on the stir plate and place the pH probe in the solution. Record each pH in the data table. Drag each beaker to the red disposal bucket when you have finished. Were your predictions correct?

Data Table

solution	pH	acidic, basic or neutral
NH_4Cl		
$NaHCO_3$		
KNO_3		
NaCN		
Na_3PO_4		

VCL 16-3: Ranking Salt Solutions by pH

In this assignment you will be asked to rank aqueous solutions of acids, bases, and salts in order of increasing pH. This is most easily done by first identifying the strong acids that have the lowest pH, the strong bases that have the highest pH, and the neutral solutions that have a pH near 7. The weak acids will have a pH between 1 and 6 and the weak bases between 8 and 14. The exact order of weak acids and weak bases is determined by comparing the ionization constants (K_a for the weak acids and K_b for the weak bases). After ranking the pH of these solutions, you will then test your predictions in the laboratory.

1. *Arrange the following 0.1 M solutions in order of increasing pH and state why you placed each solution in that position:* $NaCH_3COO$, HCl, HCN, $NaOH$, NH_3, $NaCN$, KNO_3, H_2SO_4, NH_4Cl, H_2SO_3, $NaHCO_3$, Na_3PO_4 *and* CH_3COOH.

   In order of increasing pH:

Once you have predicted the nature of each salt solution, you will use *Virtual ChemLab* to confirm your prediction. Each solution must be approximately 0.1 M for your comparisons to be valid. Most of the solutions in the Stockroom are approximately 0.1 M already. Two solutions will need to be diluted and three solutions will need to be prepared from solid salts. One of these salt solutions is already prepared and on the lab bench ready for you to measure the pH.

2. Start *Virtual ChemLab* and select *Ranking Salt Solutions by pH* from the list of assignments. The lab will open in the Titrations laboratory.

3. On the stir plate, there will be a beaker of 0.10 M ammonium chloride (NH_4Cl) that has already been prepared. The pH meter has been calibrated and is in the beaker. Record the pH of the NH_4Cl solution in the data table on the following page. When finished, drag the beaker to the red disposal bucket, and drag the bottle of NH_4Cl to the stockroom counter.

4. Click in the *Stockroom* to enter. Double-click on the NH_4Cl bottle to return it to the shelf and then double-click on the $NaHCO_3$ and KNO_3 bottles to move them to the *Stockroom* counter. Return to the laboratory

5. Open the beaker drawer (click on it) and drag a beaker to the spotlight next to the *Balance*. Click and drag the bottle of $NaHCO_3$ and place on the spot light near the balance. Click in the *Balance* area to zoom in. Place a weigh paper on the balance and tare the balance. Open the bottle by clicking on the lid (*Remove Lid*). Pick up the *Scoop* and scoop up some salt by dragging the *Scoop* to the bottle and then down the face of the bottle. Each scoop position on the face of the bottle represents a different size scoop. Pull the scoop down from the top to the second position (approximately 0.20 g) and drag it to the weigh paper in the balance until it snaps into place. Releasing the scoop places the sample on the weigh paper. Now drag the weigh paper from the balance to the beaker until it snaps into place and then empty the salt into the beaker. Return to the laboratory and drag the beaker to the stir plate.

6. Drag the 25 mL graduated cylinder to the sink under the tap until it fills. When filled, it will return to the lab bench and will indicate that it is full when you place the cursor over the cylinder. Drag the 25 mL cylinder to the beaker on the stir plate and empty it into the beaker. Place the pH probe in the beaker and record the pH in the data table. Drag the beaker to the red disposal bucket. Double-click the bottle of $NaHCO_3$ to move it to the *Stockroom* counter. Repeat steps 5 and 6 for KNO_3.

7. Click in the *Stockroom*. Double-click on the bottles of NH_3 and H_2SO_4 to move them from the shelf to the counter and return to the laboratory. Drag the bottle of NH_3 to one of the three spotlights on the lab bench. Place a beaker from the drawer on the stir plate. Drag the bottle of NH_3 to the 5 mL graduated cylinder (the smallest one) by the sink and fill the cylinder by dropping the bottle on the cylinder. Now drag the 5 mL graduated cylinder to the beaker on the stir plate and add the 5 mL of NH_3. Add 20 mL water to the beaker by filling and emptying the 10 mL cylinder into the beaker twice. Place the pH probe in the beaker and record the pH in the data table. Drag the beaker to the red disposal bucket. Double-click on the NH_3 bottle to move it back to the counter.

8. Repeat step 7 with H_2SO_4, ***except*** that you should use a 10 mL graduated cylinder of H_2SO_4 and adding 15 mL water.

9. Each of the other solutions is already approximately 0.1 M. With these solutions you can pour a small amount into the beaker that you have placed on the stir plate and place the pH probe in the solution to measure the pH. Record the pH of each solution in the data table. Drag each beaker to the red disposal bucket when you have finished. You must determine the pH for HCl, H_2SO_3, CH_3COOH (HAc), HCN, NaOH, NaCN, Na_3PO_4, and $NaCH_3COO$ (NaAc). You may take two bottles at a time from the stockroom.

Data Table

solution	pH	solution	pH
NH_4Cl		CH_3COOH (HAc)	
$NaHCO_3$		HCN	
KNO_3		NaOH	
NH_3		NaCN	
H_2SO_4		$NaCH_3COO$ (NaAc)	
HCl		Na_3PO_4	
H_2SO_3			

VCL: 17-1: Predicting the Equivalence Point

Titrations provide a method of quantitatively measuring the concentration of an unknown solution. In an acid-base titration, this is done by delivering a titrant of known concentration into an analyte of known volume. To make a titration more efficient and more accurate, it is often important to be able to predict the equivalence point for the titration. In this assignment, you will be given 0.3000 M HCl and 0.3000 M NaOH, you will predict the equivalence point, and then perform the titration to check your prediction.

1. Start *Virtual ChemLab* and select *Predicting the Equivalence Point* from the list of assignments. The lab will open in the Titrations laboratory.

2. Click the *Lab Book* to open it. Click the *Buret Zoom View* window to bring it to the front. The buret is filled with 0.3000 M NaOH. The beaker has 25.00 mL of 0.3000 M HCl. The pH meter is turned on and has been calibrated. The indicator is bromocresol green.

3. *Predict what volume (mL) of 0.3000 M NaOH is required to titrate the 25.00 mL of 0.3000 M HCl to the equivalence point.*

4. *Perform the titration.* Click the ***Save*** button in the *Buret Zoom View* window so the titration data can be saved. The horizontal position of the orange handle is off for the stopcock. Open the stopcock by pulling down on the orange handle. The vertical position delivers solution the fastest with three intermediate rates in between. Turn the stopcock to one of the fastest positions. Observe the titration curve. When the blue line in the graph window (the pH curve) begins to turn up, double-click the stopcock to turn it off. Move the stopcock down one position to add volume drop by drop.

   There are two methods for determining the volume at the equivalence point: (1) Stop the titration (close the stopcock) when a color change occurs, and then click the ***Stop*** button in the *Buret Zoom View*. A blue data link will appear in the lab book. Click the blue data link to open the *Data View* window. Scroll down to the last data entry and record the volume at the equivalence point. OR (2) Add drops slowly through the equivalence point until the pH reaches approximately 12. Click the ***Stop*** button in the *Buret Zoom View*. A blue data link will appear in the lab book. Click the blue data link to open the *Data View* window. Click ***Select All*** button to copy and paste the data to a spreadsheet program. Plot the first derivative of pH vs. volume. The peak will indicate the volume of the equivalence point since this is where the pH is changing the most rapidly as the volume changes.

5. *What volume of 0.3000 M NaOH was required by the titration to reach the equivalence point?*

   _____

6. *Calculate the percent error of the predicted volume using the formula:*

$$\%\ Error = \frac{|your\ predicted\ answer - your\ actual\ answer|}{your\ predicted\ answer} \times 100$$

$\%\ Error =$

If you want to repeat the titration, click *Exit*, select this problem from the workbook again, and repeat the experiment.

VCL 17-2: Predicting the Equivalence Point

Titrations provide a method of quantitatively measuring the concentration of an unknown solution. In an acid-base titration, this is done by delivering a titrant of known concentration into an analyte of known volume. To make a titration more efficient and more accurate, it is often important to be able to predict the equivalence point for the titration. In this assignment, you will be given 0.1276 M HCl and 0.1475 M NaOH, you will predict the equivalence point, and then perform the titration to check your prediction.

1. Start *Virtual ChemLab* and select *Predicting the Equivalence Point* from the list of assignments. The lab will open in the Titrations laboratory.

2. Click the *Lab Book* to open it. Click the *Buret Zoom View* window to bring it to the front. The buret is filled with 0.1475 M NaOH. The beaker has 25.00 mL of 0.1276 M HCl. The pH meter is turned on and has been calibrated. The indicator is bromocresol green.

3. *Predict what volume (mL) of 0.1475 M NaOH is required to titrate the 25.00 mL of 0.1276 M HCl to the equivalence poin.?*

4. *Perform the titration*. Click the ***Save*** button in the *Buret Zoom View* window so the titration data can be saved. The horizontal position of the orange handle is off for the stopcock. Open the stopcock by pulling down on the orange handle. The vertical position delivers solution the fastest with three intermediate rates in between. Turn the stopcock to one of the fastest positions. Observe the titration curve. When the blue line in the graph window (the pH curve) begins to turn up, double-click the stopcock to turn it off. Move the stopcock down one position to add volume drop by drop.

   There are two methods for determining the volume at the equivalence point: (1) Stop the titration (close the stopcock) when a color change occurs, and then click the ***Stop*** button in the *Buret Zoom View*. A blue data link will appear in the lab book. Click the blue data link to open the *Data View* window. Scroll down to the last data entry and record the volume at the equivalence point. OR (2) Add drops slowly through the equivalence point until the pH reaches approximately 12. Click the ***Stop*** button in the *Buret Zoom View*. A blue data link will appear in the lab book. Click the blue data link to open the *Data View* window. Click ***Select All*** button to copy and paste the data to a spreadsheet program. Plot the first derivative of pH vs. volume. The peak will indicate the volume of the equivalence point since this is where the pH is changing the most rapidly as the volume changes.

5. *What volume of 0.1475 M NaOH was required by the titration to reach the equivalence point?*

   _____

6. *Calculate the percent error of the predicted volume using the formula:*

$$\%\ Error = \frac{|your\ predicted\ answer - your\ actual\ answer|}{your\ predicted\ answer} \times 100$$

$\%\ Error =$

If you want to repeat the titration, click *Exit*, select this problem from the workbook again, and repeat the experiment.

VCL 17-3: Predicting the Equivalence Point

Titrations provide a method of quantitatively measuring the concentration of an unknown solution. In an acid-base titration, this is done by delivering a titrant of known concentration into an analyte of known volume. To make a titration more efficient and more accurate, it is often important to be able to predict the equivalence point for the titration. In this assignment, you will be given 0.1033 M CH_3COOH (acetic acid or HAc) and 0.1104 M NaOH, you will predict the equivalence point, and then perform the titration to check your prediction.

1. Start *Virtual ChemLab* and select *Predicting the Equivalence Point* from the list of assignments. The lab will open in the Titrations laboratory.

2. Click the *Lab Book* to open it. Click the *Buret Zoom View* window to bring it to the front. The buret is filled with 0.1104 M NaOH. The beaker has 15.00 mL of 0.1033 M HAc. The pH meter is turned on and has been calibrated. The indicator is methyl orange.

3. *Predict what volume (mL) of 0.1104 M NaOH is required to titrate the 15.00 mL of 0.1033 M HAc to the equivalence point.*

4. *Perform the titration.* Click the ***Save*** button in the *Buret Zoom View* window so the titration data can be saved. The horizontal position of the orange handle is off for the stopcock. Open the stopcock by pulling down on the orange handle. The vertical position delivers solution the fastest with three intermediate rates in between. Turn the stopcock to one of the fastest positions. Observe the titration curve. When the blue line in the graph window (the pH curve) begins to turn up, double-click the stopcock to turn it off. Move the stopcock down one position to add volume drop by drop.

   There are two methods for determining the volume at the equivalence point: (1) Stop the titration (close the stopcock) when a color change occurs, and then click the ***Stop*** button in the *Buret Zoom View*. A blue data link will appear in the lab book. Click the blue data link to open the *Data View* window. Scroll down to the last data entry and record the volume at the equivalence point. OR (2) Add drops slowly through the equivalence point until the pH reaches approximately 12. Click the ***Stop*** button in the *Buret Zoom View*. A blue data link will appear in the lab book. Click the blue data link to open the *Data View* window. Click ***Select All*** button to copy and paste the data to a spreadsheet program. Plot the first derivative of pH vs. volume. The peak will indicate the volume of the equivalence point since this is where the pH is changing the most rapidly as the volume changes.

5. *What volume of 0.1104 M NaOH was required by the titration to reach the equivalence point?*

   _____

6. *Calculate the percent error of the predicted volume using the formula:*

$$\%\ Error = \frac{|your\ predicted\ answer - your\ actual\ answer|}{your\ predicted\ answer} \times 100$$

% Error =

If you want to repeat the titration, click *Exit*, select this problem from the workbook again, and repeat the experiment.

VCL 17-4: Study of Acid-Base Titrations – Monoprotic Acids

Titrations provide a method of quantitatively measuring the concentration of an unknown solution. In an acid-base titration, this is done by delivering a titrant of known concentration into an analyte of known volume. (The concentration of an unknown titrant can also be determined by titration with an analyte of known concentration and volume.) Titration curves (graphs of volume vs. pH) have characteristic shapes. The graph can be used to determine the strength or weakness of an acid or base. The equivalence point of the titration, or the point where the analyte has been completely consumed by the titrant, is identified by the point where the pH changes rapidly over a small volume of titrant delivered. In this assignment, you will observe this titration curve by titrating the strong acid HCl with the strong base NaOH.

1. Start *Virtual ChemLab* and select *Study of Acid-Base Titrations – Monoprotic Acids* from the list of assignments. The lab will open in the Titration laboratory.

2. Click the *Lab Book* to open it. The buret will be filled with NaOH and 25.00 mL of HCl will be in the beaker with bromocresol green as an indicator. Click the ***Save*** button in the *Buret Zoom View* window. The horizontal position of the orange handle is off for the stopcock. Open the stopcock by pulling down on the orange handle. The vertical position delivers solution the fastest with three intermediate rates in between. Turn the stopcock to one of the fastest positions. Observe the titration curve. When the volume reaches 35 mL, double-click the stopcock to stop the titration. Click ***Stop*** in the *Buret Zoom View*. A blue data link will be created in the lab book. Click on it to view the titration data.

   If you need to repeat the titration, click in the *Stockroom* to enter, click on the clipboard, and select Preset Experiment #1 *Strong Acid-Strong Base*.

3. The beaker contains 0.3000 M HCl and the buret contains 0.3000 M NaOH.

   Write a complete balanced equation for the neutralization reaction between HCl and NaOH.

   _____

   The following questions can be answered by examining the *Plot* window and the *Data Viewer* window.

4. *What was the pH and color of the solution at the beginning of the titration?* _____

   _____

5. *What was the pH and color of the solution at the end of the titration?*

   _____

   _____

6. *Examine the graph of pH vs. volume (blue line) and sketch the titration curve below.*

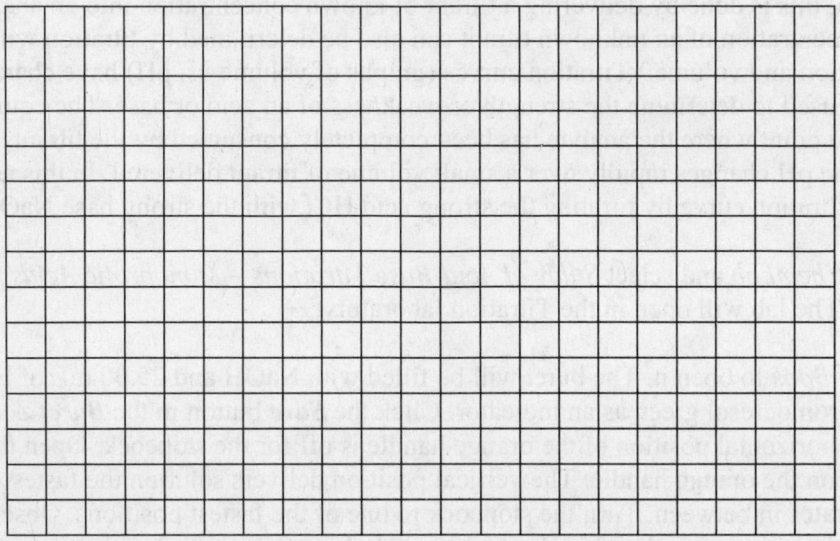

7. *What happens to the pH around 25 mL and what causes this?*

_____

_____

_____

_____

8. *Examine the graph of conductivity vs. volume (red line) and sketch the titration curve on the graph above.*

9. *What happens to the conductivity during the titration?* _____

_____

10. *What would cause the change observed in question #9?*

_____

_____

_____

_____

VCL 17-5: Weak Acid-Strong Base Titrations

Titrations provide a method of quantitatively measuring the concentration of an unknown solution. In an acid-base titration, this is done by delivering a titrant of known concentration into an analyte of known volume. Titration curves (graphs of volume vs. pH) have characteristic shapes. The equivalence point of the titration, or the point where the analyte has been completely consumed by the titrant, is identified by the point where the pH changes rapidly over a small volume of titrant delivered. In this assignment, you will observe this titration curve by titrating the weak acid CH_3COOH (acetic acid) with the strong base NaOH. You will also predict the pH at the equivalence point, validate your prediction experimentally, and then calculate the equilibrium constant for the neutralization reaction.

1. Start *Virtual ChemLab* and select *Weak Acid-Strong Base Titrations* from the list of assignments. The lab will open in the Titration laboratory.

2. Click the *Lab Book* to open it. The buret will be filled with NaOH and 25.00 mL of CH_3COOH will be in the beaker with phenolphthalein as the indicator. Click the ***Save*** button in the *Buret Zoom View* window. The horizontal position of the orange handle is off for the stopcock. Open the stopcock by pulling down on the orange handle. The vertical position delivers solution the fastest with three intermediate rates in between. Turn the stopcock to one of the fastest positions. Observe the titration curve. When the volume reaches 40 mL, double-click the stopcock to stop the titration. Click ***Stop*** in the *Buret Zoom View*. A blue data link will be created in the lab book. Click on it to view the data.

   If you need to repeat the titration, click in the *Stockroom* to enter, click on the clipboard, and select Preset Experiment # 3 *Weak Acid-Strong Base.*

3. The beaker contains 0.1894 M CH_3COOH and the buret contains 0.2006 M NaOH.

   Write a complete balanced equation for the neutralization reaction between CH_3COOH and NaOH and then write a balanced net ionic equation for this chemical reaction.

   The following questions can be answered by examining the *Plot* window, the *Data Viewer* window, and the balanced net ionic equation.

4. *Indicate the species present at the equivalence point, and predict whether the pH at the equivalence point will be pH > 7, pH < 7, or pH ≈ 7. Explain why you made this prediction.*

   _____

   _____

5. *Examine the graph of pH vs. volume (blue line) and sketch the titration curve on the following page. Mark the equivalence point as halfway between the top and bottom "shoulders" of the curve. Based on your graph, what is the pH at the equivalence point? How does it compare with your predicted pH?*

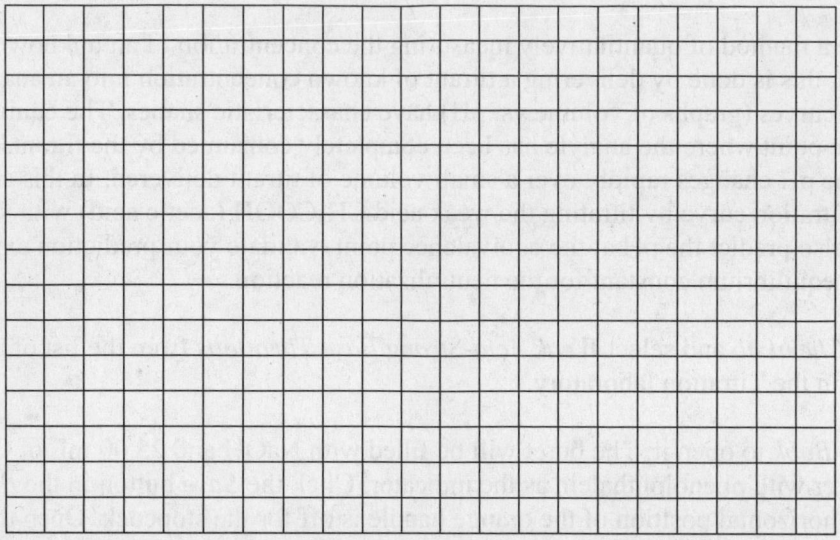

6. *Calculate the value of the equilibrium constant for the balanced net ionic equation for the weak acid-strong base titration.*

VCL 17-6: Strong Acid-Weak Base Titrations

Titrations provide a method of quantitatively measuring the concentration of an unknown solution. In an acid-base titration, this is done by delivering a titrant of known concentration into an analyte of known volume. Titration curves (graphs of volume vs. pH) have characteristic shapes. The equivalence point of the titration, or the point where the analyte has been completely consumed by the titrant, is identified by the point where the pH changes rapidly over a small volume of titrant delivered. In this assignment, you will observe this titration curve by titrating the strong acid HCl with the weak base sodium hydrogen carbonate ($NaHCO_3$). You will also predict the pH at the equivalence point, validate your prediction experimentally, and then calculate the equilibrium constant for the neutralization reaction.

1. Start *Virtual ChemLab* and select *Strong Acid-Weak Base Titrations* from the list of assignments. The lab will open in the Titration laboratory.

2. Click the *Lab Book* to open it. The buret will be filled with HCl and 25 mL of $NaHCO_3$ solution will be in the beaker with methyl orange as the indicator. Click the ***Save*** button in the *Buret Zoom View* window. The horizontal position of the orange handle is off for the stopcock. Open the stopcock by pulling down on the orange handle. The vertical position delivers solution the fastest with three intermediate rates in between. Turn the stopcock to one of the fastest positions. Observe the titration curve. When the volume reaches 40 mL, double-click the stopcock to stop the titration. Click ***Stop*** in the *Buret Zoom View*. A blue data link will be created in the lab book. Click on it to view the data.

   If you need to repeat the titration, click in the *Stockroom* to enter, click on the clipboard, and select Preset Experiment # 5 *Strong Acid-Weak Base*.

3. The beaker contains 0.40 M $NaHCO_3$ and the buret contains 0.30 M HCl.

   Write a complete balanced equation for the neutralization reaction between HCl and $NaHCO_3$ and then write a balanced net ionic equation for this chemical reaction.

   The following questions can be answered by examining the *Plot* window, the *Data Viewer* window, and the balanced net ionic equation.

4. *Indicate the species present at the equivalence point, and predict whether the pH at the equivalence point will be pH > 7, pH < 7, or pH ≈ 7. Explain why you made this prediction.*

   _____

   _____

5. *Examine the graph of pH vs. volume (blue line) and sketch the titration curve on the following page. Mark the equivalence point as halfway between the top and bottom "shoulders" of the curve. Based on your graph, what is the pH at the equivalence point? How does it compare with your predicted pH?*

6. *Calculate the value of the equilibrium constant for the balanced net ionic equation for the strong acid-weak base titration.*

VCL 17-7: Weak Acid-Weak Base Titrations

Titrations provide a method of quantitatively measuring the concentration of an unknown solution. In an acid-base titration, this is done by delivering a titrant of known concentration into an analyte of known volume. Titration curves (graphs of volume vs. pH) have characteristic shapes. The equivalence point of the titration, or the point where the analyte has been completely consumed by the titrant, is identified by the point where the pH changes rapidly over a small volume of titrant delivered. In this assignment, you will observe this titration curve by titrating the weak acid CH_3COOH (acetic acid) with the weak base NH_3. You will also predict the pH at the equivalence point, validate your prediction experimentally, and then calculate the equilibrium constant for the neutralization reaction.

1. Start *Virtual ChemLab* and select *Weak Acid-Weak Base Titrations* from the list of assignments. The lab will open in the Titration laboratory.

2. Click the *Lab Book* to open it. The buret will be filled with NH_3 and 50.00 mL of CH_3COOH is in the beaker with bromocresol purple as the indicator. Click the ***Save*** button in the *Buret Zoom View* window. The horizontal position of the orange handle is off for the stopcock. Open the stopcock by pulling down on the orange handle. The vertical position delivers solution the fastest with three intermediate rates in between. Turn the stopcock to one of the fastest positions. Observe the titration curve. When the volume reaches 25 mL, double-click the stopcock to stop the titration. Click ***Stop*** in the *Buret Zoom View*. A blue data link will be created in the lab book. Click on it to view the data.

   If you need to repeat the titration, exit the laboratory and select *Weak Acid-Weak Base Titrations* from the list of assignments.

3. The beaker contains 0.1033 M CH_3COOH and the buret contains 0.4949 M NH_3.

   Write a complete balanced equation for the neutralization reaction between CH_3COOH and NH_3.

   The following questions can be answered by examining the *Plot* window, the *Data Viewer* window, and the balanced equation.

4. *Indicate the species present at the equivalence point, and predict whether the pH at the equivalence point will be pH > 7, pH < 7, or pH ≈ 7. Explain why you made this prediction.*

   _____

   _____

   _____

5. *Examine the graph of pH vs. volume (blue line) and sketch the titration curve on the following page. Mark the equivalence point as halfway between the top and bottom "shoulders" of the curve. Based on your graph, what is the pH at the equivalence point? How does it compare with your predicted pH?*

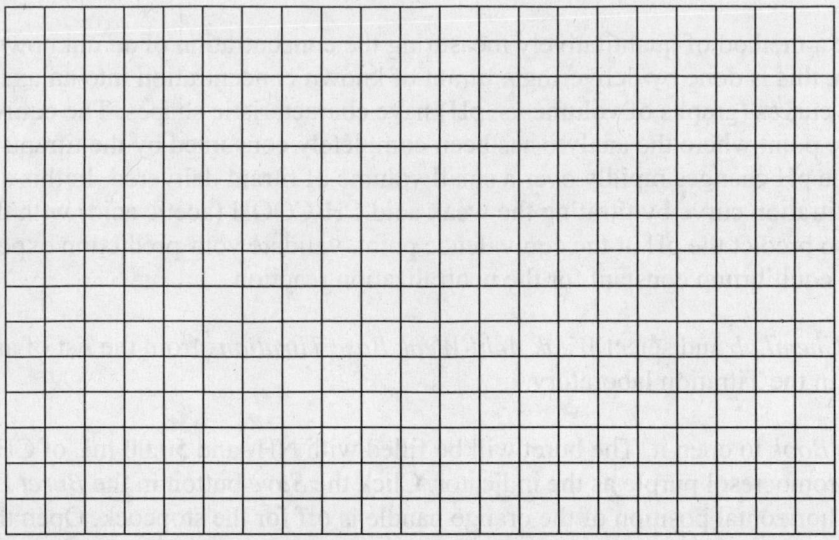

6. *Calculate the value of the equilibrium constant for the balanced net ionic equation for the weak acid-weak base titration.*

VCL 17-8: Study of Acid-Base Titrations – Polyprotic Acids

Titrations provide a method of quantitatively measuring the concentration of an unknown solution. In an acid-base titration, this is done by delivering a titrant of known concentration into an analyte of known volume. (The concentration of an unknown titrant can also be determined by titration with an analyte of known concentration and volume.) Titration curves (graphs of volume vs. pH) have characteristic shapes. The graph can be used to determine the strength or weakness of an acid or base. The equivalence point of the titration, or the point where the analyte has been completely consumed by the titrant, is identified by the point where the pH changes rapidly over a small volume of titrant delivered. For polyprotic acids, there will be multiple equivalence points. In this assignment, you will observe this titration curve by titrating the weak acid H_2SO_3 with the strong base NaOH.

1. Start *Virtual ChemLab* and select *Study of Acid-Base Titrations – Polyprotic Acids* from the list of assignments. The lab will open in the Titration laboratory.

2. Click the *Lab Book* to open it. The buret will be filled with NaOH and 25.00 mL of H_2SO_3 will be in the beaker with thymol blue as an indicator. Click the ***Save*** button in the *Buret Zoom View* window. The horizontal position of the orange handle is off for the stopcock. Open the stopcock by pulling down on the orange handle. The vertical position delivers solution the fastest with three intermediate rates in between. Turn the stopcock to one of the fastest positions. Observe the titration curve. When the volume reaches 40 mL, double-click the stopcock to stop the titration. Click ***Stop*** in the *Buret Zoom View*. A blue data link will be created in the lab book. Click on it to view the titration data.

   If you need to repeat the titration, click in the *Stockroom* to enter, click on the clipboard and select Preset Experiment #7 *Polyprotic Acid-Strong Base*.

3. The beaker contains 0.2556 M H_2SO_3 and the buret contains 0.3106 M NaOH.

   Write a complete balanced equation for the two-step neutralization reaction between H_2SO_3 and NaOH.

   The following questions can be answered by examining the *Plot* window and the *Data Viewer* window.

4. *What was the pH and color of the solution at the beginning of the titration?* _____

5. *What was the pH and color of the solution at the end of the titration? Did any additional color changes occur during the titration?*

   _____

6. *Examine the graph of pH vs. volume (blue line) and sketch the titration curve on the following page.*

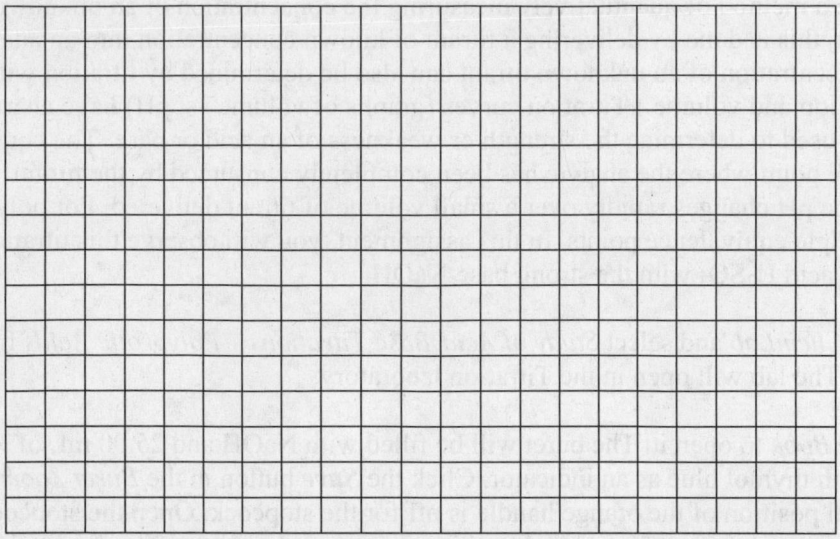

7. *What happens to the pH around 16 mL and 32 mL? What causes each to occur?*

8. *Examine the graph of conductivity vs. volume (red line) and sketch the titration curve on the graph above.*

9. *What happens to the conductivity during the titration?*

10. *What would cause the change observed in question #10?*

VCL 17-9: Acid-Base Standardization

Titrations provide a method of quantitatively measuring the concentration of an unknown solution. In an acid-base titration, this is done by delivering a titrant of known concentration into an analyte of known volume. (The concentration of an unknown titrant can also be determined by titration with an analyte of known concentration and volume.) Titration curves (graphs of volume vs. pH) have characteristic shapes. The graph can be used to determine the strength or weakness of an acid or base. The equivalence point of the titration, or the point where the analyte has been completely consumed by the titrant, is identified by the point where the pH changes rapidly over a small volume of titrant delivered. In this assignment, you will determine the molarity of an unknown solution of NaOH by titrating against a primary standard, potassium hydrogen phthalate (KHP).

1. Start *Virtual ChemLab* and select *Acid-Base Standardization* from the list of assignments. The lab will open in the Titrations laboratory.

2. Click the *Lab Book* to open it. Click the *Beakers* drawer and place a beaker in the spotlight next to the balance. Click on the *Balance* area to zoom in, open the bottle of KHP by clicking on the lid (*Remove Lid*). Drag the beaker to the balance to place it on the balance pan and tare the balance. Pick up the *Scoop* and scoop out some sample by first dragging the scoop to the mouth of the bottle and then pulling the scoop down the face of the bottle. As the scoop is dragged down the face of the bottle it will pick up different quantities of solid. Select the largest sample possible and drag the scoop to the beaker on the balance until it snaps in place and then let go. Repeat this one additional time so you have put two scoops (approximately 2 g) of KHP in the beaker. Record the mass of the sample in the data table on the following page and return to the laboratory.

3. Drag the beaker from the balance to the sink and hold it under the tap to add a small amount of water. Place it on the stir plate and drag the calibrated pH meter probe to the beaker. Add *Phenolphthalein* as the indicator.

4. The buret will be filled with NaOH. Click the ***Save*** button in the *Buret Zoom View* window so the titration data can be saved. The horizontal position of the orange handle is off for the stopcock. Open the stopcock by pulling down on the orange handle. The vertical position delivers solution the fastest with three intermediate rates in between. Turn the stopcock to one of the fastest positions. Observe the titration curve. When the blue line begins to turn up, double-click the stopcock to turn it off. Move the stopcock down one position to add volume drop by drop.

   There are two methods for determining the volume at the equivalence point: (1) Stop the titration when a color change occurs. Click the ***Stop*** button in the *Buret Zoom View*. A blue data link will appear in the lab book. Click the blue data link to open the *Data Viewer* window. Scroll down to the last data entry and record the volume at the equivalence point in the data table. OR (2) Add drops slowly through the equivalence point until the pH reaches approximately 12. Click the ***Stop*** button in the *Buret Zoom View*. A blue data link will appear in the lab book. Click the blue data link to open the *Data Viewer* window. Click the ***Select All*** button to copy and paste the data to a spreadsheet. Plot the first derivative of pH vs. volume. The peak will indicate the volume at the equivalence point since this is where the pH is changing the most rapidly as the volume changes.

   Repeat at least two additional times recording data in the data table. Do not forget to refill the buret with NaOH and place the pH meter and indicator in the beaker each time.

   The molecular weight of KHP is 204.22 g/mol.

Unknown # _____

Data Table

Trial	mass KHP (g)	volume NaOH (mL)	molarity NaOH (mol/L)
1			
2			
3			
4			
5			

5. *Write a balanced chemical equation for the reaction of KHP and NaOH.*

_____

6. *What is the average molarity of the unknown NaOH for your closest three titrations?*

_____

VCL 17-10: Analysis of Baking Soda

Titrations provide a method of quantitatively measuring the concentration of an unknown solution. In an acid-base titration, this is done by delivering a titrant of known concentration into an analyte of known volume. (The concentration of an unknown titrant can also be determined by titration with an analyte of known concentration and volume.) Titration curves (graphs of volume vs. pH) have characteristic shapes. The graph can be used to determine the strength or weakness of an acid or base. The equivalence point of the titration, or the point where the analyte has been completely consumed by the titrant, is identified by the point where the pH changes rapidly over a small volume of titrant delivered. In this assignment, you will determine the mass % of an unknown sample of baking soda ($NaHCO_3$) by titrating it with an HCl solution of known concentration.

1. Start *Virtual ChemLab* and select *Analysis of Baking Soda* from the list of assignments. The lab will open in the Titration laboratory. The laboratory will open with a beaker on the stir plate with 1.5000 g of impure solid $NaHCO_3$ and with sufficient water added to make the total volume 25.00 mL. Methyl orange indicator will have also been added to the beaker, as well as the calibrated pH meter probe.

2. Click on the *Lab Book* to open it and click on the *Buret Zoom View* window and the pH meter window to bring them to the front. The buret will be filled with 0.3015 M HCl. Click the ***Save*** button in the *Buret Zoom View* window so the titration data can be saved. The horizontal position of the orange handle is off for the stopcock. Open the stopcock by pulling down on the orange handle. The vertical position delivers solution the fastest with three intermediate rates in between. Turn the stopcock to one of the fastest positions. Observe the titration curve. When the blue line begins to turn down, double-click the stopcock to turn it off. Move the stopcock down one position to add volume drop by drop.

   There are two methods for determining the volume at the equivalence point: (1) Stop the titration when a color change occurs. Click the ***Stop*** button in the *Buret Zoom View*. A blue data link will appear in the lab book. Click the blue data link to open the *Data Viewer* window. Scroll down to the last data entry and record the volume at the equivalence point in the data table below. OR (2) Add drops slowly through the equivalence point until the pH reaches approximately 2. Click the ***Stop*** button in the *Buret Zoom View*. A blue data link will appear in the lab book. Click the blue data link to open the *Data Viewer* window. Click the ***Select All*** button to copy and paste the data to a spreadsheet. Plot the first derivative of pH vs. volume. The peak will indicate the volume at the equivalence point since this is where the pH is changing the most rapidly as the volume changes.

   Unknown sample # _____

   Data Table

mass unknown sample (g)	volume HCl (mL)	molarity HCl (mol/L)

3. *Write a balanced chemical equation for the reaction between $NaHCO_3$ and HCl.*

   _____

4. *Calculate the moles of HCl by multiplying the volume of HCl in liters and the molarity of HCl in mol/L. (Keep four significant digits in all of the calculations.)* _____

5. *The moles of HCl can be converted to moles of $NaHCO_3$ using the coefficients from the balanced equation. What is the mole to mole ratio of HCl to $NaHCO_3$? How many moles of $NaHCO_3$ are present in the sample?*

_____

6. *Calculate the grams of $NaHCO_3$ by multiplying the moles of $NaHCO_3$ by the molecular weight of $NaHCO_3$ (84.007 g/mol).*

_____

7. The mass % of $NaHCO_3$ present in the sample can be calculated by dividing the mass of $NaHCO_3$ from question #6 by the mass of the sample from the data table and multiplying by 100.

   What is the mass % of $NaHCO_3$?

_____

VCL 18-1: Identification of Cations in Solution – Flame Tests

The process of determining the composition of a sample by conducting chemical tests is called qualitative analysis. By using the appropriate tests and applying logic, the identities of the ions present in an unknown solution can be determined. A qualitative analysis scheme is typically made up of a systematic set of chemical reactions where a certain subset of the ions present in the solution are selectively precipitated and removed. The color of the precipitates and solutions provide the means to identify the ions present. Flame tests are also used to identify certain ions that are difficult to identify chemically. In this assignment, you will learn how flame tests are used to identify the cations Na^+ and K^+. As you complete this analysis, remember that careful observation and logical reasoning are the keys to a successful qualitative analysis.

1. Start *Virtual ChemLab* and select *Identification of Cations in Solution* from the list of assignments. The lab will open in the Inorganic laboratory.

2. Enter the stockroom by clicking inside the *Stockroom* window. Once inside the stockroom, drag a test tube from the box and place it on the metal test tube stand. Now click on the Na^+ bottle to add it to the test and click ***Done*** to send the test tube out to the laboratory. Repeat this process with K^+ and a Na^+/K^+ mixture. Fill one test tube with just water by clicking on the bottle of distilled water and return to the laboratory.

3. When you return to the lab you should note that you have four test tubes. Just above the periodic table there is a handle that, when clicked, pulls down the TV monitor. With the monitor down you can drag your cursor over each test tube to identify what cation is in each test tube and see a picture of what it looks like in the lower left corner of the laboratory.

4. In this assignment, you will use the ***Flame*** and ***Flame w/ Cobalt*** (cobalt glass held in front of the flame) buttons located at the bottom of the screen. Before performing any chemical test or flame test, a test tube must be moved from the blue test tube rack to the metal test tube stand. If a test tube is already present in the test tube stand, you can drag a test tube from the blue rack to the metal stand to automatically switch places.

5. *Perform a flame test with and without the cobalt filter for just the Na^+ solution. Record your observations.* _____

6. *Now do the same for just the K^+ solution and record your observations.*

   _____

7. *Now do the same for the Na^+/K^+ mixture and record your observations.* _____

   _____

8. *Now do the same with just water to get a feel for what it looks like with no chemicals other than water. Record your observations.* _____

9. Return to the *Stockroom* The bottom right shelf is called the Unknowns shelf. Click on the *Unknowns* label to reconfigure the stockroom to create a practice unknown. Click on Na^+ and K^+ and on the left

side make the minimum = 0 and maximum = 2. Click on the ***Save*** arrow to return to the regular stockroom. An unknown test tube labeled *Practice* will be placed in the blue unknown rack. Drag the practice unknown from the blue rack to the metal stand and then return to the laboratory.

10. Perform a flame test with and without the cobalt filter and determine if the practice unknown contains sodium or potassium or both or neither. To check your results, click on the *Lab Book* and on the left page, click the ***Report*** button, select the ions you think are present in the unknown, click ***Submit***, then ***Ok***. If the ion button is green, you correctly determined whether the ion was present or not. If the ion button is red you did not make the correct analysis. Return to the laboratory and click the red disposal bucket to clear the lab. If you want to repeat with a new practice unknown, return to the stockroom and retrieve it from the blue rack. Continue until you obtain only green buttons when submitted.

11. After you have finished with your practice unknowns, you are now ready to accept your assigned unknown. Clear the laboratory of any test tubes by clicking on the red disposal bucket. Return to the stockroom and then click on the clipboard hanging below the green arrow. The clipboard contains a list of test tubes containing known and unknown solutions. The unknowns are labeled with a list of possible cations followed by the unknown number. Select Preset #2, which will give you an unknown that could contain any combination of Na^+ and K^+ or both or neither. Test your assigned unknown and report the cations found in your unknown in the space below. Don't forget to record your unknown number.

Unknown _____ Cations found: _____

VCL 18-2: Identification of Cations in Solution – Ag^+, Hg_2^{2+}, Pb^{2+}

The process of determining the composition of a sample by conducting chemical tests is called qualitative analysis. By using the appropriate tests and applying logic, the identities of the ions present in an unknown solution can be determined. A qualitative analysis scheme is typically made up of a systematic set of chemical reactions where a certain subset of the ions present in the solution are selectively precipitated and removed. The color of the precipitates and solutions provide the means to identify the ions present. Flame tests are also used to identify certain ions that are difficult to identify chemically. In this assignment, you will learn the basics of a qualitative analysis scheme by performing an analysis on a mixture of Ag^+, Hg_2^{2+}, and Pb^{2+}. As you complete this analysis, remember that careful observation and logical reasoning are the keys to a successful qualitative analysis.

1. Start *Virtual ChemLab* and select *Identification of Cations in Solution* from the list of assignments. The lab will open in the Inorganic laboratory.

2. Enter the stockroom by clicking inside the *Stockroom* window. Once inside the stockroom, drag a test tube from the box and place it on the metal test tube stand. Now click on the Ag^+, Hg_2^{2+}, and Pb^{2+} bottles to add these cations to the test tube and click ***Done*** to send the test tube out to the laboratory. (There is Hg^{2+} and Hg_2^{2+} on the shelf. Make sure you obtain Hg_2^{2+}.) Return to the laboratory and click on the TV monitor handle to pull it down. As you proceed with the chemical analysis watch the TV screen to see the chemistry involved in the chemical reactions. You may also want to make some copies of your original test tube by clicking on the ***Divide*** button in case you make a mistake and need to start over.

3. Move the test tube to the metal stand. Click the NaCl reagent bottle to add chloride to the test tube.

   What observations can you make? _____

   *Click the **Centrifuge** button. What observations can you make?* _____

   Each of the three ions form insoluble precipitates (solids) with chloride. If the solution turns cloudy white it indicates that at least one of the three ions is present. Now, we must determine which one. (Remember we already know what is in the test tube, but for an unknown you won't.)

4. Turn the heat on with the ***Heat*** button. Observe the TV screen.

   What happened? If you cannot tell, turn the heat on and off while observing the TV screen.

   _____

   With the heat turned on, click ***Centrifuge*** again and then ***Decant***. (Decanting separates the solids from the solution and places the solution in the test tube rack.) Drag your cursor over the new test tube in the rack.

   What appears on the TV screen? What appears in the picture window? _____

   _____

   This is the test for Pb^{2+}. If heated, it is soluble. When cooled it becomes insoluble.

5. Turn off the ***Heat***. With the test tube containing the two remaining ions in the metal stand, click the NH_3 bottle on the reagent shelf.

   What do you observe? _____

   Addition of ammonia produces a diammine silver complex ion that is soluble. The mercury produces a green/black solid. This is the test for mercury.

6. ***Centrifuge*** and then ***Decant*** to pour the silver ion into another test tube. Move the tube with the black mercury solid to the red disposal bucket. Move the test tube containing silver back to the metal stand. Click the pH 4 reagent bottle to make the solution slightly acidic.

   What do you observe? _____

   _____

   The silver ion is soluble as the diammine silver complex ion in pH 10 and is insoluble as AgCl in pH 4. You can click alternately on each of the pH bottles to confirm this test for the silver ion.

7. Return to the *Stockroom* The bottom right shelf is called the Unknowns shelf. Click on the *Unknowns* label to reconfigure the stockroom to create a practice unknown. Click on the Ag^+, Hg_2^{2+}, and Pb^{2+} bottles and on the left side make the minimum = 0 and maximum = 3. Click on the ***Save*** arrow to return to the regular stockroom. An unknown test tube labeled *Practice* will be placed in the blue unknown rack. Drag the practice unknown from the blue rack to the metal stand and then return to the laboratory.

8. Test the *Practice* unknown and determine if it contains each of the ions Ag^+, Hg_2^{2+}, and Pb^{2+}. To check your results, click on the *Lab Book* and on the left page, click the ***Report*** button, select the ions you think are present in the unknown, click ***Submit***, then ***Ok***. If the ion button is green, you correctly determined whether the ion was present or not. If the ion button is red you did not make the correct analysis. Return to the laboratory and click the red disposal bucket to clear the lab. If you want to repeat with a new practice unknown, return to the stockroom and retrieve it from the blue rack. Continue until you obtain only green buttons when submitted.

9. After you have finished with your practice unknowns, you are now ready to accept your assigned unknown. Clear the laboratory of any test tubes by clicking on the red disposal bucket. Return to the stockroom and then click on the clipboard hanging below the green arrow. The clipboard contains a list of test tubes containing known and unknown solutions. The unknowns are labeled with a list of possible cations followed by the unknown number. Select Preset #4, which will give you an unknown that could contain any combination of Ag^+, Hg_2^{2+}, and Pb^{2+} or all of them or just water. Test your assigned unknown and report the cations found in your unknown in the space below. Don't forget to record your unknown number.

   Unknown _____ Cations found: _____

VCL 18-3: Identification of Cations in Solution – Co^{2+}, Cr^{3+}, Cu^{2+}

The process of determining the composition of a sample by conducting chemical tests is called qualitative analysis. By using the appropriate tests and applying logic, the identities of the ions present in an unknown solution can be determined. A qualitative analysis scheme is typically made up of a systematic set of chemical reactions where a certain subset of the ions present in the solution are selectively precipitated and removed. The color of the precipitates and solutions provide the means to identify the ions present. Flame tests are also used to identify certain ions that are difficult to identify chemically. In this assignment, you will learn the basics of a qualitative analysis scheme by performing an analysis on a mixture of Co^{2+}, Cr^{3+}, and Cu^{2+}. As you complete this analysis, remember that careful observation and logical reasoning are the keys to a successful qualitative analysis.

1. Start *Virtual ChemLab* and select *Identification of Cations in Solution* from the list of assignments. The lab will open in the Inorganic laboratory.

2. Enter the stockroom by clicking inside the *Stockroom* window. Once inside the stockroom, drag a test tube from the box and place it on the metal test tube stand. Now click on the *Co^{2+}*, *Cr^{3+}*, and *Cu^{2+}* bottles to add these cations to the test tube and click ***Done*** to send the test tube out to the laboratory. Return to the laboratory and click on the TV monitor handle to pull it down. As you proceed with the chemical analysis watch the TV screen to see the chemistry involved in the chemical reactions. You may also want to make some copies of your original test tube by clicking on the ***Divide*** button in case you make a mistake and need to start over.

3. *Move the test tube to the metal stand. Click the NaOH bottle on the reagent shelf. What observations can you make?* _____

   _____

4. Click ***Centrifuge*** and ***Decant***. (Decanting separates the solids from the solution and places the solution in the test tube rack.)

   What observations can you make as you drag your cursor over each test tube? _____

   _____

   This is the test for chromium. If the new test tube in the blue rack is green when decanted then chromium is present. You can confirm it by placing the clear green test tube in the metal stand and clicking pH 10 and then adding HNO_3.

   What observations can you make? _____

   _____

5. With the test tube containing the cobalt and copper precipitate in the metal stand, add NH_3.

   What observations can you make? _____

   _____

6. ***Centrifuge*** and ***Decant***. Add HNO_3 to the tube in the metal stand containing the precipitate.

   What observations can you make? _____

   _____

   This is the confirmatory test for cobalt ion (Co^{2+}).

7. Place the test tube from the blue rack, which is the solution from step # 5, in the metal stand. Add HNO_3.

   What observations can you make? _____

   _____

   This is the confirmatory test for copper.

8. Return to the *Stockroom*. The bottom right shelf is called the Unknowns shelf. Click on the *Unknowns* label to reconfigure the stockroom to create a practice unknown. Click on the Co^{2+}, Cr^{3+}, and Cu^{2+} bottles and on the left side make the minimum = 0 and maximum = 3. Click on the ***Save*** arrow to return to the regular stockroom. An unknown test tube labeled *Practice* will be placed in the blue unknown rack. Drag the practice unknown from the blue rack to the metal stand and then return to the laboratory.

9. Test the *Practice* unknown and determine if it contains each of the ions Co^{2+}, Cr^{3+}, and Cu^{2+}. To check your results, click on the *Lab Book* and on the left page, click the ***Report*** button, select the ions you think are present in the unknown, click ***Submit***, then ***Ok***. If the ion button is green, you correctly determined whether the ion was present or not. If the ion button is red you did not make the correct analysis. Return to the laboratory and click the red disposal bucket to clear the lab. If you want to repeat with a new practice unknown, return to the stockroom and retrieve it from the blue rack. Continue until you obtain only green buttons when submitted.

10. After you have finished with your practice unknowns, you are now ready to accept your assigned unknown. Clear the laboratory of any test tubes by clicking on the red disposal bucket. Return to the stockroom and then click on the clipboard hanging below the green arrow. The clipboard contains a list of test tubes containing known and unknown solutions. The unknowns are labeled with a list of possible cations followed by the unknown number. Select Preset #6, which will give you an unknown that could contain any combination of Co^{2+}, Cr^{3+}, and Cu^{2+} or all of them or just water. Test your assigned unknown and report the cations found in your unknown in the space below. Don't forget to record your unknown number.

    Unknown _____ Cations found: _____

VCL 18-4: Identification of Cations in Solution – Ba^{2+}, Sr^{2+}, Ca^{2+}, Mg^{2+}

The process of determining the composition of a sample by conducting chemical tests is called qualitative analysis. By using the appropriate tests and applying logic, the identities of the ions present in an unknown solution can be determined. A qualitative analysis scheme is typically made up of a systematic set of chemical reactions where a certain subset of the ions present in the solution are selectively precipitated and removed. The color of the precipitates and solutions provide the means to identify the ions present. Flame tests are also used to identify certain ions that are difficult to identify chemically. In this assignment, you will need to develop your own qualitative analysis scheme to separate and identify the Group II cations Ba^{2+}, Sr^{2+}, Ca^{2+}, and Mg^{2+}. As you complete this analysis, remember that careful observation and logical reasoning are the keys to a successful qualitative analysis.

1. Start *Virtual ChemLab* and select *Identification of Cations in Solution* from the list of assignments. The lab will open in the Inorganic laboratory.

2. Enter the stockroom by clicking inside the *Stockroom* window. Once inside the stockroom, drag a test tube from the box and place it on the metal test tube stand. Now click on the Ba^{2+}, Sr^{2+}, Ca^{2+}, and Mg^{2+} bottles to add these cations to the test tube and click ***Done*** to send the test tube out to the laboratory. Return to the laboratory and click on the TV monitor handle to pull it down. As you proceed with the chemical analysis watch the TV screen to see the chemistry involved in the chemical reactions. You may also want to make some copies of your original test tube by clicking on the ***Divide*** button in case you make a mistake and need to start over.

3. *What do the solubility rules tell you about the way to separate the second group of cations? How can you tell each of the ions in this group apart? Think about changing the temperature and the pH. Design your own qualitative scheme for identification of these four Group II ions and write it below. Experiment with each of the four ions alone and then in combinations. Test an unknown to see if you can really determine the presence or absence of each of the four ions in this group.*

4. Return to the *Stockroom*. The bottom right shelf is called the Unknowns shelf. Click on the *Unknowns* label to reconfigure the stockroom to create a practice unknown. Click on the Ba^{2+}, Sr^{2+}, Ca^{2+}, and Mg^{2+} bottles and on the left side make the minimum = 0 and maximum = 4. Click on the ***Save*** arrow to return to the regular stockroom. An unknown test tube labeled *Practice* will be placed in the blue unknown rack. Drag the practice unknown from the blue rack to the metal stand and then return to the laboratory.

5. Test the *Practice* unknown and determine if it contains each of the ions Ba^{2+}, Sr^{2+}, Ca^{2+}, and Mg^{2+}. To check your results, click on the *Lab Book* and on the left page, click the ***Report*** button, select the ions you think are present in the unknown, click ***Submit***, then ***Ok***. If the ion button is green, you correctly determined whether the ion was present or not. If the ion button is red you did not make the correct analysis. Return to the laboratory and click the red disposal bucket to clear the lab. If you want to repeat with a new practice unknown, return to the stockroom and retrieve it from the blue rack. Continue until you obtain only green buttons when submitted.

6. After you have finished with your practice unknowns, you are now ready to accept your assigned unknown. Clear the laboratory of any test tubes by clicking on the red disposal bucket. Return to the stockroom and then click on the clipboard hanging below the green arrow. The clipboard contains a list of test tubes containing known and unknown solutions. The unknowns are labeled with a list of possible cations followed by the unknown number. Select Preset #8, which will give you an unknown that could contain any combination of Ba^{2+}, Sr^{2+}, Ca^{2+}, and Mg^{2+} or all of them or just water. Test your assigned unknown and report the cations found in your unknown in the space below. Don't forget to record your unknown number.

Unknown_____ Cations found: _____

VCL 18-5: Identification of Cations in Solution – Co^{2+}, Cu^{2+}, Ni^{2+}

The process of determining the composition of a sample by conducting chemical tests is called qualitative analysis. By using the appropriate tests and applying logic, the identities of the ions present in an unknown solution can be determined. A qualitative analysis scheme is typically made up of a systematic set of chemical reactions where a certain subset of the ions present in the solution are selectively precipitated and removed. The color of the precipitates and solutions provide the means to identify the ions present. Flame tests are also used to identify certain ions that are difficult to identify chemically. In this assignment, you will need to develop your own qualitative analysis scheme to separate and identify the transition metal cations Co^{2+}, Cu^{2+}, and Ni^{2+}. As you complete this analysis, remember that careful observation and logical reasoning are the keys to a successful qualitative analysis.

1. Start *Virtual ChemLab* and select *Identification of Cations in Solution* from the list of assignments. The lab will open in the Inorganic laboratory.

2. Enter the stockroom by clicking inside the *Stockroom* window. Once inside the stockroom, drag a test tube from the box and place it on the metal test tube stand. Now click on the Co^{2+}, Cu^{2+}, and Ni^{2+} bottles to add these cations to the test tube and click ***Done*** to send the test tube out to the laboratory. Return to the laboratory and click on the TV monitor handle to pull it down. As you proceed with the chemical analysis watch the TV screen to see the chemistry involved in the chemical reactions. You may also want to make some copies of your original test tube by clicking on the ***Divide*** button in case you make a mistake and need to start over.

3. *What do the solubility rules tell you about the way to separate the second group of cations? How can you tell each of the ions in this group apart? Think about changing the temperature and the pH. Design your own qualitative scheme for identification of these three transition metal ions and write it below. Experiment with each of the three ions alone and then in combinations. Test an unknown to see if you can really determine the presence or absence of each of the three ions in this group.*

4. Return to the *Stockroom*. The bottom right shelf is called the Unknowns shelf. Click on the *Unknowns* label to reconfigure the stockroom to create a practice unknown. Click on the Co^{2+}, Cu^{2+}, and Ni^{2+} bottles and on the left side make the minimum = 0 and maximum = 3. Click on the ***Save*** arrow to return to the regular stockroom. An unknown test tube labeled *Practice* will be placed in the blue unknown rack. Drag the practice unknown from the blue rack to the metal stand and then return to the laboratory.

5. Test the *Practice* unknown and determine if it contains each of the ions Co^{2+}, Cu^{2+}, and Ni^{2+}. To check your results, click on the *Lab Book* and on the left page, click the ***Report*** button, select the ions you think are present in the unknown, click ***Submit***, then ***Ok***. If the ion button is green, you correctly determined whether the ion was present or not. If the ion button is red you did not make the correct analysis. Return to the laboratory and click the red disposal bucket to clear the lab. If you want to repeat with a new practice unknown, return to the stockroom and retrieve it from the blue rack. Continue until you obtain only green buttons when submitted.

6. After you have finished with your practice unknowns, you are now ready to accept your assigned unknown. Clear the laboratory of any test tubes by clicking on the red disposal bucket. Return to the stockroom and then click on the clipboard hanging below the green arrow. The clipboard contains a list of test tubes containing known and unknown solutions. The unknowns are labeled with a list of possible cations followed by the unknown number. Select Preset #10, which will give you an unknown that could contain any combination of Co^{2+}, Cu^{2+}, and Ni^{2+} or all of them or just water. Test your assigned unknown and report the cations found in your unknown in the space below. Don't forget to record your unknown number.

   Unknown _____ Cations found: _____

VCL 19-1: The Balance Between Enthalpy and Entropy

For chemical reactions, we say that a reaction proceeds to the right when ΔG is negative and that the reaction proceeds to the left when ΔG is positive. At equilibrium ΔG is zero. The Gibbs-Helmholtz equation specifies that at constant temperature $\Delta G = \Delta H - T\Delta S$ or, in other words, that the sign and size of ΔG is governed by the balance between enthalpic (ΔH) and entropic (ΔS) considerations. In this assignment, you will dissolve several different salts in water, measure the resulting temperature changes, and then make some deductions about the thermodynamic driving forces behind the dissolving process.

1. Start *Virtual ChemLab* and select *The Balance Between Enthalpy and Entropy* from the list of assignments. The lab will open in the Calorimetry laboratory.

2. There will be a bottle of sodium chloride (NaCl) on the lab bench. A weigh paper will be on the balance with approximately 2 g of NaCl on the paper.

3. The calorimeter will be on the lab bench and filled with 100 mL water. Click on the *Lab Book* to open it. Make certain the stirrer is ***On*** (you should be able to see the shaft rotating). In the thermometer window click ***Save*** to begin recording data. Allow 20-30 seconds to obtain a baseline temperature of the water.

4. Drag the weigh paper with the sample to the calorimeter until it snaps into place and then pour the sample in the calorimeter. Observe the change in temperature until it reaches a maximum (or minimum) and then record data for an additional 20-30 seconds. (You can click the clock on the wall labeled *Accelerate* to accelerate the time in the laboratory.) Click ***Stop***. A blue data link will appear in the Lab Book. Click the data link and record the temperature before adding the NaCl and the *highest* or *lowest* temperature after adding the NaCl in the data table.

5. Click the red disposal bucket to clear the lab. Click on the *Stockroom* to enter. Click on the clipboard and select Preset Experiment #7 and repeat the experiment with $NaNO_3$. Record the initial and final temperatures in the data table.

6. Click the red disposal bucket to clear the lab. Click on the *Stockroom* to enter. Click the clipboard and select Preset Experiment #8 and repeat the experiment with $NaCH_3COO$ (NaAc). Record the initial and final temperatures in the data table.

Data Table

Mixture	T_1	T_2	ΔT (T_2-T_1)
NaCl (s) + H_2O (l)			
$NaNO_3$ (s) + H_2O (l)			
$NaCH_3COO$ + H_2O (l)			

Use your experimental data to answer the following questions:

7. *Calculate ΔT ($\Delta T = T_2 - T_1$) for each mixture and record the results in the data table.*

8. An exothermic process releases heat (warms up), and an endothermic process absorbs heat (cools down).

   Which solutions are endothermic and which are exothermic? What is the sign of the change in enthalpy, ΔH, in each case?

   _____

9. *Which solution(s) had little or no change in temperature?* _____

10. When sodium chloride dissolves in water, the ions dissociate:

$$NaCl\,(s) = Na^{+}\,(aq) + Cl^{-}\,(aq)$$

   Write ionic equations, similar to the one above, that describe how $NaNO_3$ and $NaCH_3COO$ each dissociate as they dissolve in water. Include heat as a reactant or product in each equation.

   _____

   _____

11. *What is the sign of the change in Gibbs free energy (ΔG) for each process?*

   _____

12. *Consider the Gibbs-Helmholtz equation, $\Delta G = \Delta H - T\Delta S$. For each dissolving process, substitute the signs of ΔG and ΔH into the equation and predict the sign for the entropy (ΔS). Does the sign for entropy change seem to make sense? Explain.*

   _____

   _____

   _____

   _____

13. *If the sign for ΔG is negative (spontaneous process) and the sign for ΔS is positive (more disorder) for both dissolving processes, how could one be endothermic (positive ΔH) and one be exothermic (negative ΔH)? Is there more to consider than just the dissolving process?*

   _____

   _____

   _____

   _____

   _____

   _____

   _____

   _____

VCL 20-1: Study of Oxidation-Reduction Titrations

Titrations provide a method of quantitatively measuring the concentration of an unknown solution. This is done by delivering a titrant of known concentration into an analyte of known volume. (The concentration of an unknown titrant can also be determined by titration with an analyte of known concentration and volume.) In oxidation-reduction (redox) titrations, the voltage resulting from the mixture of an oxidant and reductant can be measured as the titration proceeds. The equivalence point of the titration, or the point where the analyte has been completely consumed by the titrant, is identified by the point where the voltage changes rapidly over a small volume of titrant delivered. In this assignment, you will observe this titration curve by titrating $FeCl_2$ with $KMnO_4$.

1. Start *Virtual ChemLab* and select *Study of Oxidation-Reduction Titrations* from the list of assignments. The lab will open in the Titrations laboratory.

2. The buret will be filled with $KMnO_4$ and a solution containing $FeCl_2$ will be in the beaker on the stir plate. The horizontal position of the orange handle is off for the stopcock. Open the stopcock by pulling down on the orange handle. The vertical position delivers volume the fastest with three intermediate rates in between. Turn the stopcock to one of the fastest positions. Observe the titration curve. When the volume reaches 45 mL double-click the stopcock to turn it off.

3. Examine the graph of voltage vs. volume (blue line) and sketch the titration curve below. Label the axes.

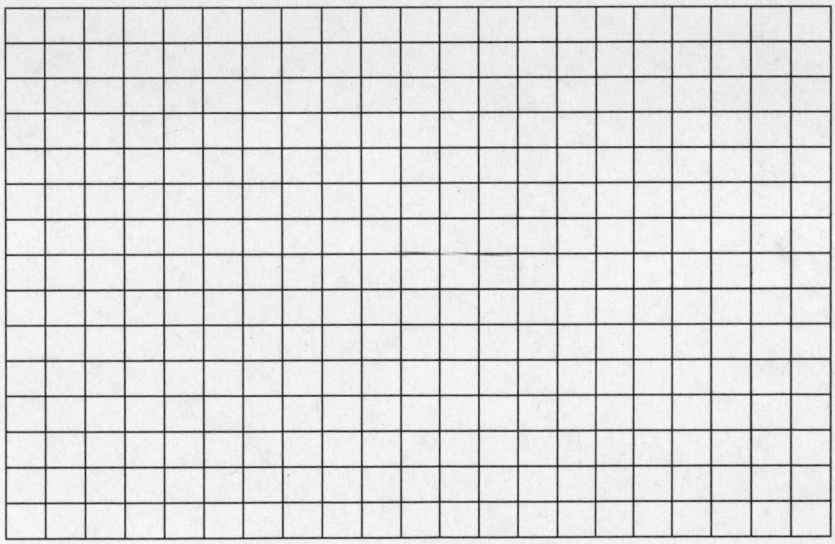

4. *Write a balanced net ionic equation for the reaction in acidic solution of $FeCl_2$ and $KMnO_4$ (Fe^{2+} becomes Fe^{3+} and MnO_4^- becomes Mn^{2+}).*

5. The reduction potential of Fe^{2+} is 0.732 volts, and the reduction potential of MnO_4^- in acidic solution is 1.507 volts.

   If you titrate $KMnO_4$ into $FeCl_2$, what happens to the voltage of the solution as the titration starts and proceeds to the end?

   _____

VCL 20-2: Standardization of a Permanganate Solution

Titrations provide a method of quantitatively measuring the concentration of an unknown solution. This is done by delivering a titrant of known concentration into an analyte of known volume. (The concentration of an unknown titrant can also be determined by titration with an analyte of known concentration and volume.) In oxidation-reduction (redox) titrations, the voltage resulting from the mixture of an oxidant and reductant can be measured as the titration proceeds. The equivalence point of the titration, or the point where the analyte has been completely consumed by the titrant, is identified by the point where the voltage changes rapidly over a small volume of titrant delivered. In this assignment, you will determine the molarity of an unknown solution of $KMnO_4$ by titrating against a primary standard, solid As_2O_3.

1. Start *Virtual ChemLab* and select *Standardization of a Permanganate Solution* from the list of assignments. The lab will open in the Titrations laboratory.

2. Click the *Lab Book* to open it. Click the *Beakers* drawer and place a beaker in the spotlight next to the balance. Click on the *Balance* area to zoom in, open the bottle of As_2O_3 by clicking on the lid (*Remove Lid*). Drag the beaker to the balance to place it on the balance pan and tare the balance. Pick up the *Scoop* and scoop out some sample by first dragging the scoop to the mouth of the bottle and then pulling the scoop down the face of the bottle. As the scoop is dragged down the face of the bottle it will pick up different quantities of solid. Select the second sample size from the top and drag the scoop to the beaker on the balance until it snaps in place and then let go. You should have approximately 0.1 g of As_2O_3 in the beaker. Record the mass of the sample in the data table on the following page and return to the laboratory.

3. Drag the beaker from the balance to the sink and hold it under the tap to add a small amount of water. Place it on the stir plate and add the voltmeter probe to the beaker.

4. The buret will be filled with a solution of $KMnO_4$ of unknown concentration. A bottle of permanganate is on the lab bench. Record the unknown sample number. Click the ***Save*** button in the *Buret Zoom View* window so the titration data can be saved. The horizontal position of the orange handle is off for the stopcock. Open the stopcock by pulling down on the orange handle. The vertical position delivers solution the fastest with three intermediate rates in between. Turn the stopcock to one of the fastest positions. Observe the titration curve. When the blue line begins to turn up, double-click the stopcock to turn it off. Move the stopcock down one position to add volume drop by drop.

   There are two methods for determining the volume at the equivalence point: (1) Stop the titration when a color change occurs. Click the ***Stop*** button in the *Buret Zoom View*. A blue data link will appear in the lab book. Click the blue data link to open the *Data Viewer* window. Scroll down to the last data entry and record the volume at the equivalence point in the data table. OR (2) Add drops slowly through the equivalence point until the voltages reaches a maximum and levels off. Click the ***Stop*** button in the *Buret Zoom View*. A blue data link will appear in the lab book. Click the blue data link to open the *Data Viewer* window. Click the ***Select All*** button to copy and paste the data into a spreadsheet program. Plot the first derivative of voltage vs. volume. The peak will indicate the volume at the equivalence point since this is where the voltage is changing the most rapidly as the volume changes.

   To repeat the titration, drag the beaker to the red disposal bucket, move a new beaker from the beaker drawer next to the balance, and repeat the procedure. Do not forget to refill the buret with $KMnO_4$ and place the voltmeter in the beaker each time.

The molecular weight of As_2O_3 is 197.84 g/mol.

Unknown # _____

Data Table

Trial	mass As_2O_3 (g)	volume $KMnO_4$ (mL)	molarity $KMnO_4$ (mole/L)
1			
2			
3			
4			
5			

5. Upon the addition of water, As_2O_3 is converted to H_3AsO_3. During the titration H_3AsO_3 is oxidized to H_3AsO_4 and MnO_4^- is reduced to Mn^{2+}.

   Write a balanced net ionic equation for the reaction.

6. *Using the information in the data table, calculate the molarity of the permanganate solution. (Note that 1 mole of As_2O_3 solid becomes 2 moles of H_3AsO_3 when dissolved in water.)*

VCL 20-3: Analysis of a Ferrous Chloride Sample

Titrations provide a method of quantitatively measuring the concentration of an unknown solution. This is done by delivering a titrant of known concentration into an analyte of known volume. (The concentration of an unknown titrant can also be determined by titration with an analyte of known concentration and volume.) In oxidation-reduction (redox) titrations, the voltage resulting from the mixture of an oxidant and reductant can be measured as the titration proceeds. The equivalence point of the titration, or the point where the analyte has been completely consumed by the titrant, is identified by the point where the voltage changes rapidly over a small volume of titrant delivered. In this assignment, you will determine the mass % of an unknown sample of ferrous chloride ($FeCl_2$) by titrating it with a $KMnO_4$ solution of known concentration.

1. Start *Virtual ChemLab* and select *Analysis of a Ferrous Chloride Sample* from the list of assignments. The lab will open in the Titrations laboratory.

2. Record the $FeCl_2$ Unknown number in the data table on the following page. Click the *Lab Book* to open it. Click the *Beakers* drawer and place a beaker in the spotlight next to the balance. Click on the *Balance* area to zoom in, open the bottle of unknown $FeCl_2$ by clicking on the lid (*Remove Lid*). Drag the beaker to the balance to place it on the balance pan and tare the balance. Pick up the *Scoop* and scoop out some sample by first dragging the scoop to the mouth of the bottle and then pulling the scoop down the face of the bottle. As the scoop is dragged down the face of the bottle it will pick up different quantities of solid. Select the largest sample size and drag the scoop to the beaker on the balance until it snaps in place and then let go. Repeat this again so you have approximately 2 g of unknown in the beaker. Record the unknown number and the mass of the sample in the data table. (You will have to drag the $FeCl_2$ bottle to the front of the lab bench to see the unknown number.) Return to the laboratory.

3. Place the beaker on the stir plate. Drag the 50 mL graduated cylinder under the tap in the sink and fill it with distilled water. It will automatically snap back into place when it is full. Drag the full 50 mL graduated cylinder to the beaker on the stir plate and then pour the water into the beaker. Now place the voltmeter probe in the beaker and make sure the voltmeter is on.

4. The buret will be filled with 0.0815 M $KMnO_4$. Click the ***Save*** button in the *Buret Zoom View* window so the titration data can be saved. The horizontal position of the orange handle is off for the stopcock. Open the stopcock by pulling down on the orange handle. The vertical position delivers solution the fastest with three intermediate rates in between. Turn the stopcock to one of the fastest positions. Observe the titration curve. When the blue line begins to turn up, double-click the stopcock to turn it off. Move the stopcock down one position to add volume drop by drop.

   There are two methods for determining the volume at the equivalence point: (1) Stop the titration when a color change occurs. Click the ***Stop*** button in the *Buret Zoom View*. A blue data link will appear in the lab book. Click the blue data link to open the *Data Viewer* window. Scroll down to the last data entry and record the volume at the equivalence point in the data table. OR (2) Add drops slowly through the equivalence point until the voltage reaches a maximum and levels off. Click the ***Stop*** button in the *Buret Zoom View*. A blue data link will appear in the lab book. Click the blue data link to open the *Data Viewer* window. Click the ***Select All*** button to copy and paste the data into a spreadsheet program. Plot the first derivative of voltage vs. volume. The peak will indicate the volume at the equivalence point since this is where the voltage is changing the most rapidly as the volume changes.

5. Repeat the titration at least two additional times recording your data in the data table. Do not forget to refill the buret with $KMnO_4$, place the voltmeter probe in the beaker, and add water each time.

The molecular weight of $FeCl_2$ is 151.91 g/mol.

Unknown # _____

Data Table

Trial	mass $FeCl_2$ (g)	volume $KMnO_4$ (mL)	molarity $KMnO_4$ (mol/L)
1			
2			
3			
4			
5			

6. *Write a balanced net ionic equation for the reaction in acidic solution of $FeCl_2$ and $KMnO_4$ (Fe^{2+} is oxidized to Fe^{3+} and MnO_4^- is reduced to Mn^{2+}).*

7. The moles of MnO_4^- can be calculated by multiplying the volume of MnO_4^- required to reach the endpoint multiplied by the molarity of the MnO_4^- solution.

What are the moles of MnO_4^- used in the titration? _____

8. The moles of $FeCl_2$ can be calculated by using the mole ratio from the balanced equation.

How many moles of $FeCl_2$ were in the unknown? _____

9. The mass of $FeCl_2$ in the sample can be calculated by multiplying the moles of $FeCl_2$ by the molecular weight of $FeCl_2$.

What is the mass of $FeCl_2$ in the sample? _____

10. The mass % of $FeCl_2$ in the unknown sample can be calculated by dividing the mass of $FeCl_2$ in the sample by the total mass of the unknown sample.

What is the % $FeCl_2$ in your unknown sample? _____

11. *What is the average % iron in the unknown sample using your best three answers?*

_____